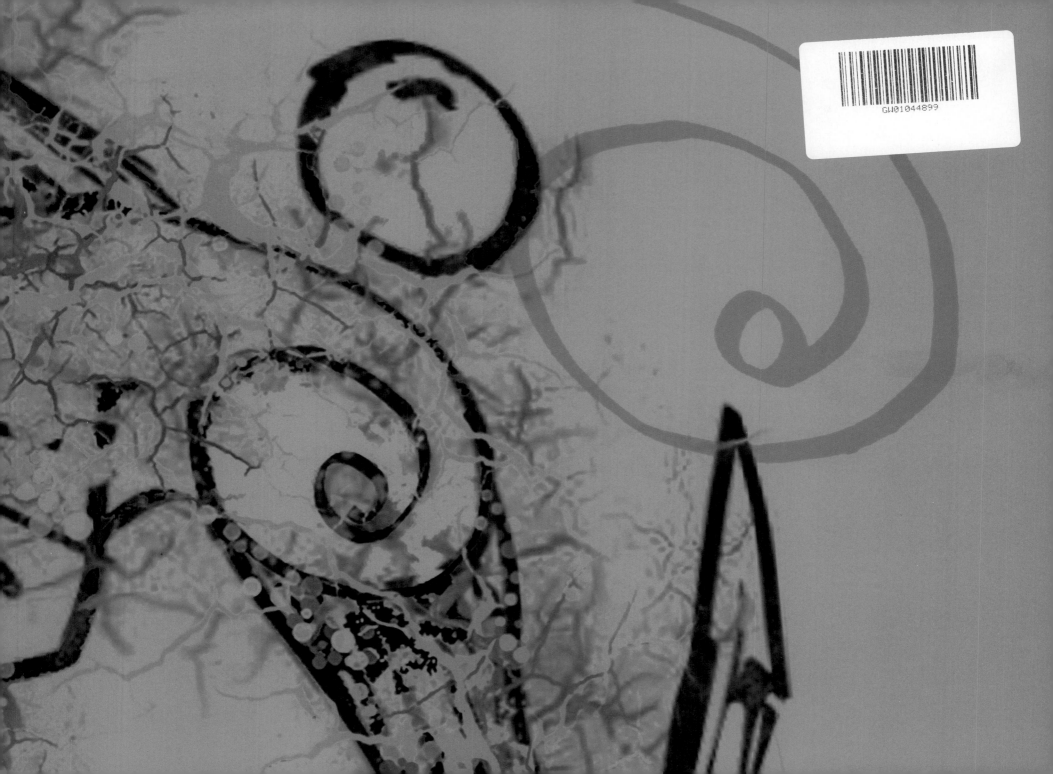

GW01044899

Finding Me Beyond Illness

Finding Me Beyond Illness

My creative story:
Exploring art, illness
and identity

Dr Shanali Perera

Changing Lanes

'See yourself through art. Be inspired. Be visible. Be heard.'

Acknowledgments

The existence of this book is mainly due to the support Devinda and Ian gave me to publish it. They have played a big part in my path towards recovery; they are my 'shimmering conduits'. Their invaluable feedback and input have influenced and helped me. I cannot thank them enough.

I also want to take this opportunity to thank my inner circle, my parents, immediate family and friends. Without their love and support, I would not have been able to make this journey on my own. They have been beacons of light in my darkest hours, energising me with the fuel that propels me forward. All have my enormous gratitude.

I count myself extremely fortunate to have formed so many meaningful relationships in my life – with friends, family, work colleagues and acquaintances. I wish to thank every person that has helped me, in large or small part, in the course of my illness. Each has laid a brick to build the foundation of my new path.

My parents gave me the freedom to speak my mind and encouraged me to express my thoughts freely. They taught me how to think creatively and critically from an early age. Their strength, guidance and belief are what made me who I am today. I hope I have made them proud. I thank them.

Art and the human experience

This book is dedicated to everyone living with or making sense of illness – their own or other people's – and to my inner circle, who have been with me every step of the way.

Thank you for sharing your time. To find out more about me and my work, contact me at:

✉ shanaliperera@gmail.com

🌐 www.shanaliperera.com

🌐 www.changinglanes.me

🐦 @shanaliperera2

f @changinglanes.me

📷 @shanaliperera2

On the cover: *Onwards*, 2020
Opposite: *Proximity*, 2018

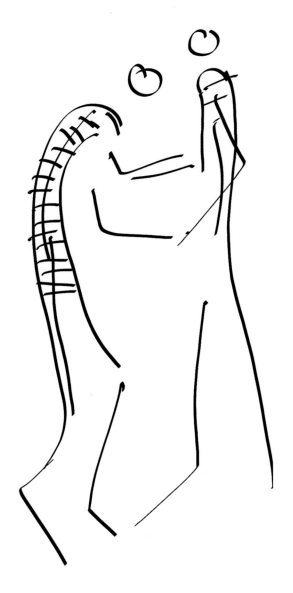

'The aim of art is to represent not
the outward appearance of things,
but their inward significance.'

Aristotle

Contents

Opposite: *Harmony,* 2019

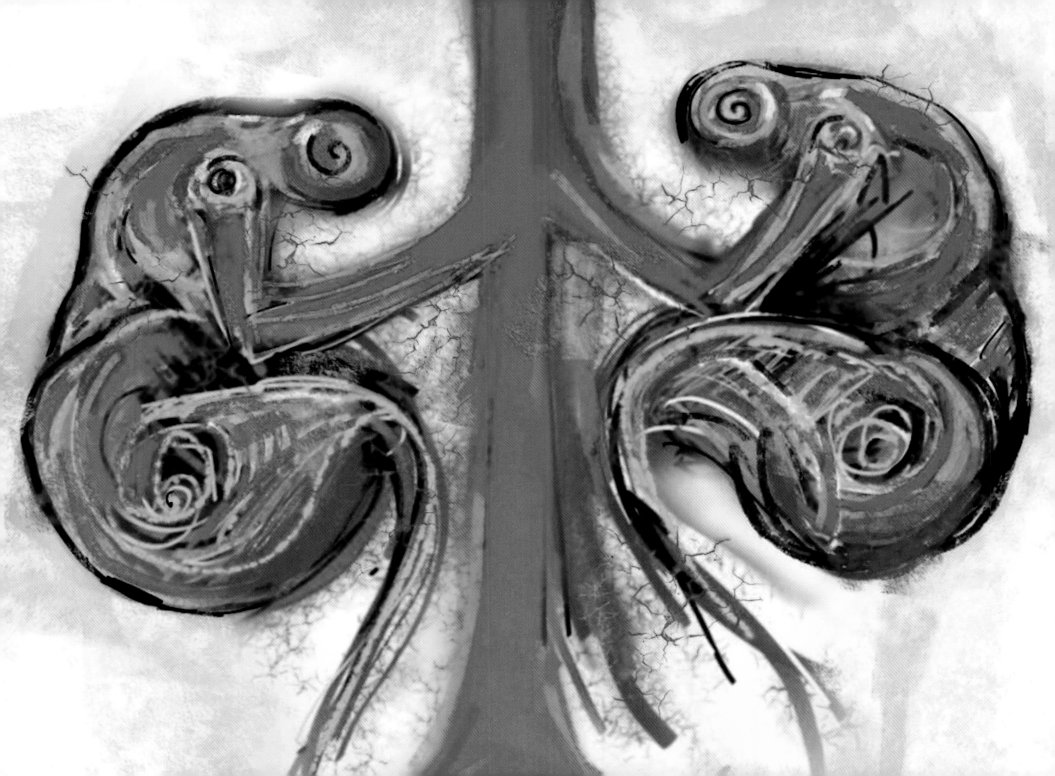

Preface

This is a story about creative empowerment. I took up digital art following early retirement due to a rare condition called vasculitis that came on during my specialist training in rheumatology. Vasculitis causes inflammation in the blood vessels in different parts of the body. In my case, it affects my hand function and mobility, amongst other things, and I have been using an app on my phone to create art to cope with the illness experience, pain and all the changes that came along with it. I thought I would give you all a snapshot of my journey of using art to transform the illness experience into a more meaningful way of living as I moved from being a clinician to becoming a patient in my own specialty. For me, this form of artistic expression is a means of self-exploration. It conveys how I am feeling and what I am going through. By creating digital canvases, I use colour to capture and portray my illness journey. As a self-taught artist, patient and former rheumatologist, it is my interpretation of what pain and lived experience looks like. Being both a doctor and a patient, I had the opportunity to gain a unique perspective on art and the human experience. It can be rather difficult to sum up or verbalise what I am going through at times, something that many people living with complex long-term conditions will understand.

The concept of my work revolves around capturing and representing my personal experience, reflecting moments of meaning along the way. I use colour, shape and lines as a method to document my observations and portray energies surrounding pain, fatigue, and my everyday changes living with illness in an attempt to objectify the subjective. The illness is the subjective component that describes the patient's experience of the disease. Pain is subjective. Change is subjective. Our individual experience and perception of it, how we connect

with it inwardly and outwardly, varies. My own relationship with illness, with pain, changes as a concept and a process; how it makes me act and feel has prompted me to explore this further with my art.

My art is my take on expressing the mind and body experience of anticipation, uncertainty, challenges, concerns, effects on life . . . all the things that accompany the illness trajectory. How does it look and what does it feel like as a bodily experience? My art is an attempt to find symmetry within my asymmetric inner chaos. The bigger picture is to go beyond the physical, to show the face behind the illness. I cannot control how my illness evolves nor how it affects my day. I can, however, control what I create. Art has helped me find the sense of order and control that have helped me move forward with my life. Here, I'm sharing the ongoing impact art has in enabling me to take control and manage my long-term condition so that others can hopefully benefit from it: patients, carers and health practitioners.

My work is centred around exploring art and the human factor in order to open a dialogue and create agency about facilitating what I call 'expressions of illness' across intersections of art, health, medical education and patient support. Using my medical background and my patient experience, I am interested in looking at how visual arts can help us further explore the human aspect of medical practice. I want to generate a wider interest of how artistic expressions of the lived experience can help health practitioners and the public gain new insights beyond patients' illnesses. My aim is to show how visual expressions can be an alternate language, opening new ways of seeing to help clinicians gain a deeper understanding of what people go through, the impact illnesses have on a person's image and identity. Ideally, I hope to show

that art can expose the hidden, invisible inner world of illness and help narrow the gap between 'medical science and the human experience'.

This book is a distillation of my art combined with an eclectic overview of my thoughts, generating along the way ideas and awareness to ponder on. I am connecting and communicating with you to contribute my experience of coping with challenges and, hopefully, collaborate with you to evoke change.

Throughout the book, I touch on different areas in order to:

- highlight the role art can play in the self-management of chronic illness

- reflect on the role art can play in self-expression, health and well-being

- gain a deeper understanding, explore ways of seeing and learn about one's self: art is a tool that can aid the process of self-development

- examine the role of art in medical communication, patient interaction and healthcare, showing, in effect, how art can be a powerful tool to communicate the physical, emotional, social and spiritual impact of illness so that healthcare providers can build up a better understanding, open newer ways of seeing and learn more about patients

- give people a better understanding about living with illness and its influence on identity and lifestyle – this involves confronting prejudice, stereotyping and stigma

There is overlap in these areas, with important themes recurring through all of them. I dive in and out of these issues in various sections of the book. I use repetition to emphasise the importance of key phrases and ideas such as 'making the invisible visible', 'finding symmetry', 'shifting dynamics' and 'image and identity', which all have meaning to me as I consider my life from a new perspective, finding me beyond illness. I invite you to read this book with an open mind, willing to receive, consider and reflect on varying perspectives and unexpected insights. Look at the colour, form and movement in the art, centring your attention on the key role visual representation can play in understanding, expressing and communicating – to oneself and others. The art pieces may resonate with you, or maybe it's the drawings that will give you something to ponder on. I hope above all you take something from my multifaceted experience from the pages that follow to help you, my fellow traveller, on your own journey through life.

Beyond the fog

The murky haze of illness looms over
like heavy clouds before rain

The thick fog of uncertainty, apprehension and change
weighs heavy like iron shackles around my legs

Like the silver lining to every cloud
Emerges the 'face of resilience'

Helping me to see beyond the fog
Helping me to confront the chaos of uncertainty
Helping me to tackle vulnerability and isolation
Helping me to maintain balance and harmony within

The dots slowly start to align
Lifting the haze and fog away
Bringing me back into focus

'I stumble, I fall, I break, I mend, I get back up
I walk past Life's stolen moments
Shadows that haunt of shattered dreams
Glimpsing reflections of who I was

I feel triumphant as I face them all
The calm, the storm and the in-between days
Living each day, I meet life
Life meets me, I dare to hope...'

Opposite: *Beyond the Fog*, 2016

At times, words are not enough to communicate experiences

How have I used art to connect, communicate and transform the narrative of my illness? Exploring art and the human factor, my visual narrative aims to:

- Open dialogue, raise awareness and create agency about facilitating expressions of illness

- Show how visual expressions can be an alternate language, communicating the clinical process and complexities of the lived experience with illness to a wider audience

- Open ways of knowing and learning to help healthcare professionals get a deeper understanding of what people go through

'I found I could say things with colour and shapes that I couldn't say any other way – things I had no words for.'

Georgia O'Keeffe

Digital expressions of my illness experiences

Often with illness, pain or change, finding the words to describe how you feel is a challenge in itself. In this instance, would visually accepting pain or change make a difference to the person describing it?

For me, being able to construct the concept and process into a structure, by giving it shape and form, made it visible. This visibility helped me to better understand and accept the changes brought on by the illness – both through the act of creating an image and in the final image itself. It also showed what I was going through in another dimension, opening ways to communicate with myself and others. I believe that engaging in art, making it or viewing it can truly help to reveal and convey the illness experience.

I have explored the digital medium to:

- Capture the essence of being a patient

- Create expressions of illness

- Make sense of illness

- Cope with illness

- Build endurance

- Deal with pain

- Combat fatigue

- Construct a refuge from which to tackle change

Opposite: *Life Stills*, 2016
Right: *Support*, 2019

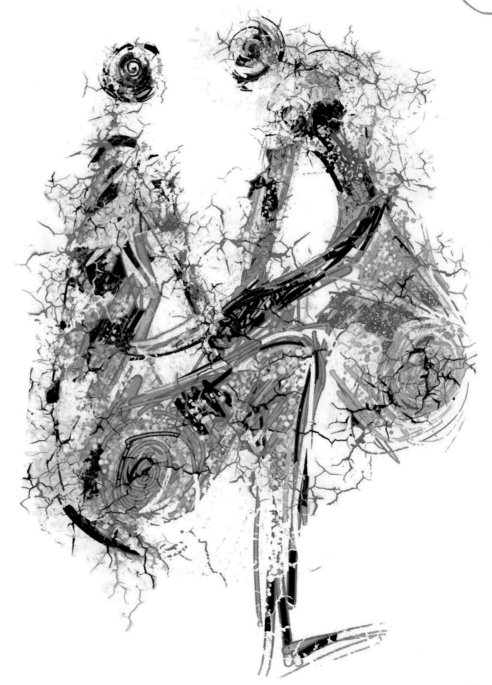

13

What the lines and shapes of my drawings signify

The images I create can often, and at first sight, appear random or formless, especially the abstract ones. But once you 'decode' the thinking behind my drawings, I hope their meanings will start to become clear and the messages will reveal themselves to you.

I use lines to convey movement, communication and complexity within my invisible inner world. You may notice that spirals feature heavily in a lot of my work, especially in my figurative images and around their head, shoulders, hips, and ankles. This is because spirals for me are a symbol of continuity and flow in the midst of pain, chaos, uncertainty and limitations in mobility. The circular, symmetrical and repetitive movements in these concentric lines strangely catch the harmony within all those fluctuations in my inner rhythm. They also represent the constant struggle to achieve a steady state. The same applies to zigzag lines, triangles and starbursts. Wavy lines and curves, meanwhile, represent resilience.

The body shapes are my interpretation of how pain, fatigue, anticipation, uncertainty, change, concerns and all the emotions that accompany the illness trajectory look and feel like both as inner-body and out-of-body experiences. The body posturing also denotes this mind/body experience. The physical positions signify interconnections, support and collective strength.

Circles usually indicate hope, while 'sharper' shapes such as triangles, squares and dots represent pain and frustration. *I Am Fatigue* (opposite) is a good example of how I try to express, in this example, frustration, agitation and exasperation with all those dots, lines, zigzags and sharp angles.

'If you hear a voice within you say, "You cannot paint," then by all means paint, and that voice will be silenced.'

Vincent Van Gogh

Opposite: *I Am Fatigue*, 2019

Exploring the healing energy of colour

'Colour is a power which directly influences the soul. Colour provokes a psychic vibration. Colour hides a power still unknown but real, which acts on every part of the human body.'

Wassily Kandinsky

How we perceive colour and what each colour means to us varies from person to person as well as from culture to culture. Our reaction to a certain colour is personal: our connection to it is deeply rooted in our individual experiences. Humans have always tapped into the healing power of colour. It's a millennia-old concept known as chromotherapy, which was practised in Ancient Greece, Egypt, China and India.

In their academic study 'A Critical Analysis of Chromotherapy and Its Scientific Evolution' (Evidence-Based Complementary and Alternative Medicines, 2005), Samina Azeemi and S. Mohsin Raza explain how the practice of chromotherapy dates back as far as 2000 BC. The Egyptians utilised sunlight as well as colour for healing. People of that era used primary colours (i.e., red, blue and yellow) for healing, as they were unaware of the mixing of two colours. The ancient Indian Ayurvedic physician Charaka, who lived in sixth century BC, recommended sunlight to treat a variety of diseases. In ancient Greece, the physical nature of colour was dominant. Colour was intrinsic to healing, which involved restoring balance. Colour therapy entertains the idea that vibrational frequencies of colour have an impact on human health and wellness. Our universe is full of vibrational energy. The rate at which a substance vibrates determines its density or form as matter. Physical matter are substances that vibrate slowly. When the vibration is at high frequency, it appears as light.

Light is energy, and the phenomenon of colour is a product of the interaction of energy and matter. Each colour of light on the visible and invisible spectrum has a unique frequency, wavelength and fixed amount of energy that denominates as a distinct colour. The human eye is sensitive only to a small segment of wavelengths called the visible spectrum or visible light. The human eye translates these wavelengths into the seven colours of the rainbow: violet, indigo, blue, green, yellow, orange and red. These visual colours with their unique wavelength and oscillations, when combined with a light source and selectively applied to different parts of the body, provide the necessary healing energy required by the body to treat both mental and physical health conditions. Under these assumptions, colour theory believes light can interact with the atoms of the human body to provide health, wellness, and therapeutic benefits.

Many ancient medicinal traditions used these electrical impulses and magnetic currents to direct human health through colour-based therapeutic approaches.

This ancient tradition is today the source of a growing number of scientific studies exploring the mechanisms behind chromotherapy and their possible therapeutic applications. Far from being an outdated belief, there's a growing body of thought that colour can indeed be used as part of the healing process physically, mentally and spiritually.

Opposite: *Make Isolation Bright,* 2020

I use art to unlock the emotional power of colour and tap into my human resilience. For me, there is one colour in particular that has a special resonance. It has the ability to provide comfort during stressful and upsetting moments or offer hope and be a motivator. It can also be empowering. This colour can also depict the angry nature of the beasts within, of pain, fatigue and chaos. As strange as it may sound, I embrace the duality of this colour, the destruction it represents as well as the comfort it brings. In a way, it demonstrates the positives that can be drawn from negative situations. I am talking about the colour red.

It's only very recently that I have found out about chromotherapy and the symbolic meanings that individual colours have for our subconscious. I was absolutely fascinated to find out that red is the most scientifically studied primary colour, and I was at last able to understand my subconscious connection to it. According to colour therapy, red light is 'the great energiser' and is also an effective pain reliever. Red goes beyond the surface of the skin and to the core of where the pain is coming from. Red increases blood flow, increasing oxygen levels that help your body to heal.

After discovering chromotherapy, I was even more surprised to come across the work of Edwin Babbitt. An American physician and the author of *The Principles of Light and Colour* (1878), he was an early proponent of colour therapy and identified the colour red as a stimulant, notably of blood and, to a lesser extent, the nerves. Given that my underlying condition affects blood vessels and nerves, this really grabbed my attention. You will see my affinity to red throughout this book, with its accompanying affiliations to pain and inflammation. The same applies to orange, purple, pink and yellow, which all sit at the same end of the stimulatory spectrum for me. And, as in art, so in life: my devotion to red extends beyond my paintings and my phone and tablet cover; my gloves, hats, coats and trainers are all that colour, too. This is something that's only happened in the last few years.

Blue, green and white show a sense of calm, peace, hope and contentment. I use black to emphasise a darker mood. The variation in colour fields, hues and different colour filters capture the fluctuating emotional energies, mood change, mystery and intrigue.

But of course it's not as simple as that. There are times when I don't know why an image develops in the way that it does. It only gradually becomes clearer and more detailed. My past memories and subconscious feelings, along with what I am experiencing at that given moment, all play a role in generating an image. The colours I tend to pick when I do my figures are almost always chosen subconsciously. It's not an exact science, and what I have explained here is only what I think – or perhaps what I think I think. You may well see my images differently, and that is as it should be. All art is open to interpretation.

'Colour is the keyboard, the eyes are the hammers, the soul is the piano with many strings. The artist is the hand that plays, touching one key or another purposively, to cause vibrations in the soul.'

Wassily Kandinsky

Opposite: *Symmetry*, 2018

Introduction: The story begins

It is March 2009. Birmingham, UK. I was an active, healthy second-year specialist trainee in rheumatology. Having relocated from a quaint garden flat in Cheltenham just six months earlier, I was looking forward to enjoying life in an exciting new city. I had come to Birmingham to take up a full-time position under the West Midlands deanery. I was on the fast track, my heart set on pursuing a career in a fascinating specialism and getting ready for whatever life had in store for me.

The unforeseen chaos that followed after my sudden admission to hospital, emergency surgery and an unrelated set of brand-new symptoms knocked me off the fast track. Roles shifted. I became a patient in my own specialty. My daily routine took a 180-degree turn. All of a sudden, I lost all the functional independence and freedom I had taken for granted. I found myself at a crossroads, not knowing where – or how – to go next.

Living with a chronic illness can turn your life upside down, gradually changing the landscape of daily living. After numerous hospital admissions, consultations and examinations, I realised I was changing from a doctor to a patient, and I began to see what the illness journey was like from that perspective. Facing everyday struggles is a lot different when you find yourself sitting on the opposite side of the doctor's desk for the first time. Until then, diagnosing and managing conditions was more of a black-and-white reality for me; now I was a patient, everything was many shades of grey. My priorities changed. Now it was all about coping, adapting, adjusting.

'Challenges are gifts that force us to search for a new centre of gravity. Don't fight them. Just find a new way to stand. Turn your wounds into wisdom.'

Oprah Winfrey

Opposite: *Layers Within*, **2015**
Dealing with multiple layers all at once.

Emotional turmoil
Physical illness
Cultural norms
Social expectations
Work
Spiritual beliefs
Perceptions
Attitudes
Relationships

Attitudes and relationships

The adventure began with 'once was' becoming 'now is', as daily life took on a variety of new forms. The presence of a life-altering condition changes everything: you put yourself on hold, and things come to a standstill. Then, you begin to adapt. Living with an unexpected, out-of-the-blue illness doesn't become any easier, but, over time, it becomes part and parcel of your day. The resulting personal and professional transformation redefined me. Responsibilities altered, my priorities were revised and my self-identity was reshaped.

Going through the challenges patients experience first-hand was both a revealing and a humbling experience. Dealing with multiple elements all at once – physical, emotional, spiritual, work-related, social, relationship-based – was like having ten different screens open at once on my laptop and no user's guide showing me what to do. Next, uncertainty joined the party. Not knowing what the next step was or what was going on led to such a sinking feeling. At times, I felt like a fraud: I kept saying that my hands and legs were going numb and painful on repeated use, yet there was nothing to see apart from intermittent lesions on my toes and nailfold haemorrhages. I looked well, yet a myriad of symptoms plagued me. I felt powerless and unable to control the direction my life was heading.

It took years to get on top of my management. After a facial nerve palsy, multiple foot drops, wrist drops and double incontinence, I was finally treated for vasculitis. This is a rare disease that causes inflammation of the blood vessels. Any blood vessel in different parts of the body can be affected.

Inflammation is our immune system's natural response to injury or infection. But in the case of vasculitis, for some reason the immune system attacks healthy blood vessels, causing them to become swollen and narrow. These changes can restrict blood flow, resulting in poor flow to tissues throughout the body, such as the lungs, brain, kidneys, nervous system and skin. In my case, it affects my hand function and mobility, amongst other things. I was also diagnosed with postural tachycardia syndrome (PoTS), part of an autonomic neuropathy. PoTS is an abnormal increase in a person's heart rate that happens after sitting up or standing. Usually when we sit up or stand, gravity pulls some of our blood to our hands, feet and abdomen. Responding to that, our blood vessels narrow, increasing the heart rate slightly to maintain blood flow to the heart and brain, and thus preventing a drop in blood pressure. This is all done involuntarily by the autonomic nervous system – the part of the nervous system in charge of regulating body functions we don't need to think about such as breathing, heart rate and digestion. In PoTS, the autonomic nervous system does not work properly. There's a drop in blood supply to the heart and brain when a person becomes upright, and the heart rate quickly increases to compensate. Finding out I had PoTS was life-altering. Simply standing up and walking a few yards became a challenge. After years of varied health environments, numerous multidisciplinary medical consults, I came to realise that the new baseline I've been striving to find is but a shadow that keeps changing shape with time. What does the short, intermediate or long-term future hold for me?

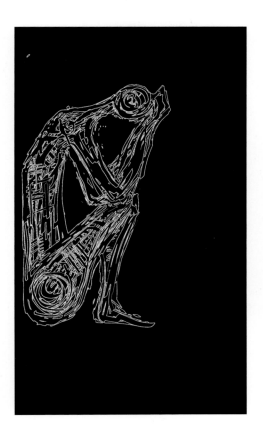

***Dealing With Multiple Layers*, 2017**
This work is called *Dealing With Multiple Layers* and its three aspects
convey separate variants of one feeling: uncertainty. The different
colour filters show how the varying degrees of uncertainty affect
changes in mood as a bodily experience. Uncertainty is governed
by the fact that the direction my life is heading is unknown, bringing
with it a sense of helplessness tied into being unable to meet personal
expectations. The bent head held between the hands depicts this
helplessness, not knowing what to do, not knowing how to feel.

Illustrating the challenges that build up as time goes on

After many failed attempts at returning to work, switching from full-time to part-time training, taking countless periods out over three years, I finally had to take ill-health retirement. I felt betrayed, robbed of all my dreams and life expectations. Shattered aspirations flew out of the window.

Unable to achieve the standards my pre-ill self set for me, I felt left behind by friends and colleagues. I was subjected to all sorts of social expectations and pressures, and I felt isolated and vulnerable. Most of all, the illness completely distorted my self-image and identity: both my inner image of 'who I was' and 'what I am meant to be' and my outer image of 'what I looked like'. The person I saw in the mirror changed after I gained weight due to the medication I was taking, my dress sizes continuing to keep jumping upwards. I found it hard to relate to myself as my personal sense of fashion disappeared out of the window. At first, I even found it hard to recognise myself because of the disfigurement caused by my facial palsy. Fortunately, this only lasted a few weeks, and my features returned to near normal. But the facial muscles on the left side of my face still tire after overuse: for example, if I talk for long periods, the lower left part of my face droops a little, the side of my mouth slants downwards and my speech becomes a little slurry. Sometimes, there will be a slight drooling of saliva from that corner of my mouth. I do recover quite quickly now after resting the face muscles, and it's something I can laugh about and carry on with my talk if I am at a presentation, but at first, and for a long time, it was something I found very difficult to handle. In addition, when my heart rate was not properly controlled I couldn't maintain a conversation for long. I would feel faint, ready to pass out, and I would have to crouch on the floor to increase the blood supply to my brain. I began telling people when I felt light-headed that I was about to have a 'crouchy'. I don't know why, but I named it after the film *Crouching Tiger, Hidden Dragon.*

As all this happened I gradually lost 'me', the person I was and what I stood for. I changed from 'I' to 'me the illness' as I succumbed to a state of powerlessness and loss of control. How I got over this was by discovering the creative process. It helped me in two ways. First, the artistic experience allowed me to express and symbolise feelings about the illness as a whole-person involvement. It revealed my tug of war with the illness, helping me to see what was going on, what I was going through in dealing with my symptoms, treatments, emotions and the constant change. It gave a structure and form to my situation and enabled me to notice things I hadn't seen at first, as though I was entering a building I'd only ever seen from the outside. Visualising the illness process this way showed me an alternate perspective, helping me to understand and acknowledge and come to terms with the 'what is' of my present reality rather than the 'what was' that had come before. Second, making art helped me realise that I could not control how the illness was evolving or what that did to my day. I could, however, control what I created, which gave me a sense of achievement, a sense of purpose. The focus shifted to what I could do rather than what I couldn't. All this helped me to regain some level of control. This was the turning point, and I decided from now on to defy being defined by my illness and begin to evolve into a newer version of me. I had discovered the path that would lead to *finding me beyond illness.*

> 'I really think a champion is defined not by their wins but by how they can recover when they fall.'
>
> Serena Williams

illness

Pain

Fatigue

Dealing with symptoms

Feeling powerless

Loss of control

Limited functional independence

Day to day variability and disruption of routine

Additional conditions: severe endometriosis, asthma

Emotions: anger, frustration

Feeling betrayed by my body

Treatment burden

Reaction to diagnosis

Denial, difficulty coping

My inner Reality, 2019
Summing up the challenges I faced at
the onset of my illness – the physical and
mental burdens of disease and treatment.

The struggle with my sociopolitical-cultural self

Feeling betrayed by medicines and the health system

Feeling betrayed by life's expectations and my emotions

Feeling betrayed by society

Exclusion and feelings of helplessness due to cultural attitudes and beliefs

Social isolation and an inability to deal with social pressures

Struggle with myself

Self-reliance

Self-identity lost

Unable to uphold self-worth

Self-image distorted

Low self-confidence

Right: *Life Stills*, 2016
Recapping the inner struggles I
experienced when enduring the illness.

Opposite: *Layers Within*, 2017
Illustrating the challenges that
build up as time goes on.

As the illness overtakes life with its collateral insults, dealing with the unforeseen chaos that follows can be hard work. As the balance slowly tips over, it can become overwhelming.

Personal attitudes, fears, influences from cultural and spiritual beliefs, especially in pluralistic and secular societies, can feed off and reinforce each other in a vicious circle. This makes the illness experience an emotionally draining encounter.

It becomes a struggle to uphold your personal standards when self-image feels distorted, self-identity is lost and self-worth is low. Trying to find a balance between my old self and my new self was a challenge, going from someone who was confident, in control, financially independent and self-reliant to the complete opposite.

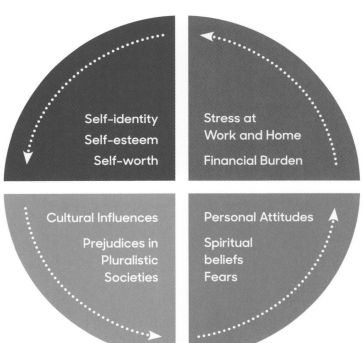

Self-identity
Self-esteem
Self-worth

Stress at
Work and Home
Financial Burden

Cultural Influences
Prejudices in
Pluralistic
Societies

Personal Attitudes
Spiritual
beliefs
Fears

What is the inspiration behind my work?

Given that so much of the human experience around unwellness is steeped in emotion and complexity, the focus of my art is on understandings of identity, art and illness. I create digital canvases using colour to document my observations and capture the different energies surrounding the *essence* of being a patient and the many shades of my everyday existence, giving visibility and voice to my journey with vasculitis. My visual expressions are my interpretation as an artist, patient and former rheumatologist on what pain looks like and how to represent living with and making sense of vasculitis. It's my attempt to objectify the subjective, a way of abstracting what happens behind the scenes on the disease journey. Above all, it's the creation of an alternate language to help others see beyond the physical and understand my daily transitions with illness in colour.

Being both a doctor and a patient gave me a unique opportunity to reflect on art and the human experience, to think about how illness can distort our sense of self. Articulating this experience, especially with complex and layered long-term conditions, can be rather difficult at times. My form of artistic expression is a means of self-exploration to convey how I'm feeling. Art has helped me redefine myself after illness distorted my identity and image.

I am a self-taught artist with no formal training. My art comes from within. Emotions, pain, fatigue and even humour are my cues for expressing the changes around me. I use art as a form of self-inquiry to document my observations, reflections, adaptations, transitions, identity and attitude. It's a way of looking at the impact illness has on me and my lifestyle in colour and shape. Art gives visibility and voice to my inner journey with illness as an artist, a vasculitis patient, and a retired clinician in rheumatology.

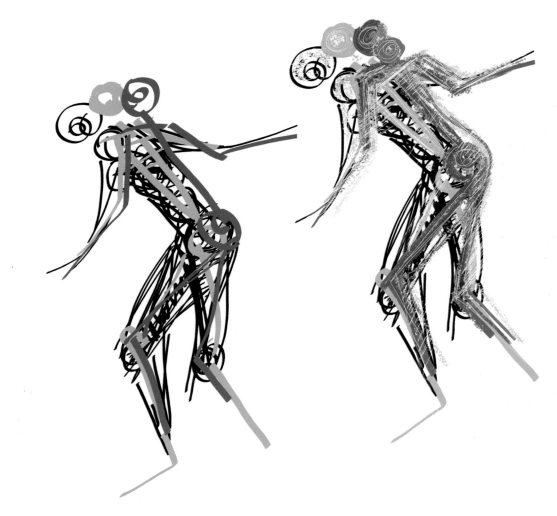

'Finding symmetry within my asymmetric inner chaos.'

Overlap

The concept of *Overlap* is the idea that I am not one person one day and a different person the next but that there are transitions and overlap between who I am from day to day.

I try to capture that shifting focus and the energies surrounding me with my artwork; some elements stay the same and others change. Fatigue may be a limiting factor one day: pain may be more severe the next. They overlap only to differ in intensity.

The changes in my inner rhythm and mood are depicted by different colours, lines, shapes and tones.

Opposite: *Inner Rhythm*, 2019
Right: *Overlap*, 2019

Below and opposite: *Overlap*, **2019** I look at different versions of my self, along my illness journey, using shades and tones to capture the different vibes surrounding me. In these two images some elements are the same, while others have changed, as have the colours and the 'feel'. And between them there is overlap.

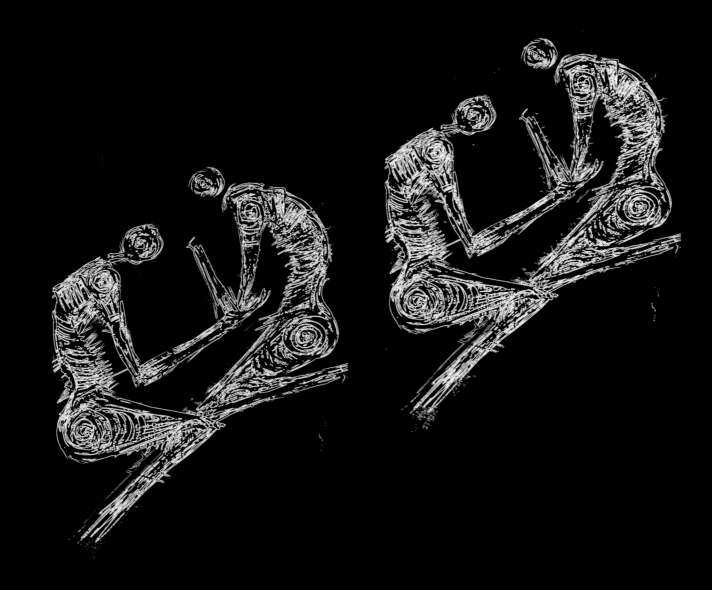

What is distinctive about my art?

My art brings together conceptions of art, medicine and humanity through my experience as a clinician, patient and creator. In doing so, my work captures and illustrates physiological and psychological flexibility, the flow maintaining inner balance, embodied perspective of resilience, the unlocking of energies – emotion, pain, change, fatigue – the inner reality of illness, and the outer reality of pain, fatigue and change.

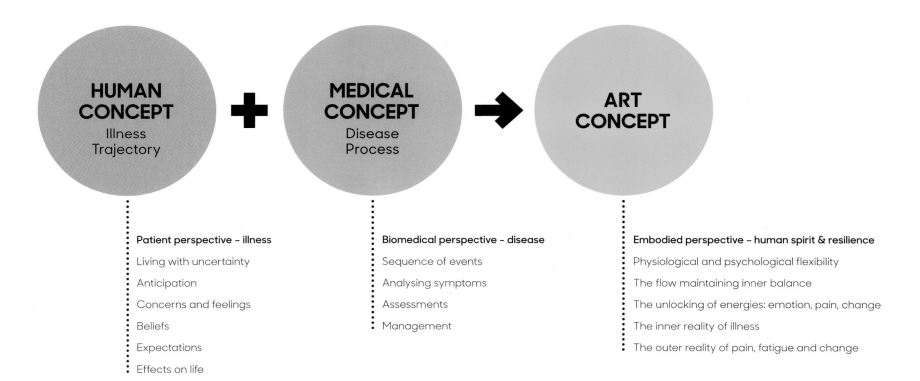

HUMAN CONCEPT
Illness Trajectory

+

MEDICAL CONCEPT
Disease Process

→

ART CONCEPT

Patient perspective – illness

Living with uncertainty

Anticipation

Concerns and feelings

Beliefs

Expectations

Effects on life

Biomedical perspective – disease

Sequence of events

Analysing symptoms

Assessments

Management

Embodied perspective – human spirit & resilience

Physiological and psychological flexibility

The flow maintaining inner balance

The unlocking of energies: emotion, pain, change

The inner reality of illness

The outer reality of pain, fatigue and change

Interconnections, 2019

Why I use the digital medium

I started exploring the digital medium to create art with the emphasis on coping and adjusting around illness. On repeated use of my hands they become numb, dead painful, cramp-like. The pain goes up my arm to my shoulder, and I have to stop every so often to rest. Using traditional methods like oil on canvas, watercolour or charcoal is too difficult for me. The digital medium was my adaptation to this problem.

An app on my phone and tablet enabled me to draw and create art with minimal physical effort and less pain and fatigue than when using a paintbrush on canvas or charcoal on paper. It's not completely comfortable or pain-free, but it is bearable. This newfound freedom the app gave me is what led to my present work. Using an app on my mobile phone to produce digital art had a transformative impact on my ability to manage my unexpected illness. I'm hoping that you will appreciate the pain my artwork reveals as well as the pain it caused to produce it.

The role of the digital medium in long-term illness and disability

People with certain conditions have to deal with not only the general disability of the chronic illness but also the physical limitations when trying to render the art that is in their mind. For those like me with limited functional capacity or pain in their hands, making digital art is a useful and liberating way to explore one's creative side and to cope with the struggles of day-to-day life.

Today, rapid developments in both healthcare and digital technology are changing the world at an ever-increasing pace. Digital media has transformed social networking, allowing wider interaction, collaboration and sharing through a variety of platforms and forums. There is room to further expand the role of the digital medium for creative expression as a holistic approach to care, given the wealth of studies illustrating the beneficial effects of integrating creativity and health. I am working towards conveying the impact that using the digital medium to draw has had on transforming my lifestyle, supporting me to take control and manage my rare long-term condition.

What I hope to achieve through my art

It's been more than 10 years since my diagnosis. Today, I believe it is time to present my personal dialogue of being a digital artist, educator, patient and retired clinician, to explain how I use art to communicate hard-to-articulate experiences, raise awareness, start conversations and create agency about facilitating expressions of illness. With this personal account, I'm sharing my inner reality, the complexity and the fluid state of my lived experience. Creative empowerment through digital art has helped me to cope, express a broad range of emotions and transform the illness experience into a more meaningful way of living as I moved from being a clinician to a patient.

My work is centred around exploring art and the human factor, to raise awareness about creative engagement and finding tools such as art to combat the challenges of the illness experience, along with other therapies. From my experience, adapting to find ways around limitations plays a key role in rebuilding confidence. Learning new ways to take charge and finding new tools to help with stress can certainly help deal with situations better. Having a tool, be it art, gardening, cooking or music, for example, can work alongside other therapies and medicines to cope with pain, fatigue and other everyday battles. Then, sharing your digital art, if that's what you choose, breaks the isolation and can also help others understand your emotions and empathise with your pain, fatigue and illness.

See yourself through art

Expressing illness through art is its own language, one that's open to interpretation to whoever experiences it. The insights it offers to clinicians in particular are a new way of seeing, showing what the creator has to put up with and how illness can affect a person's image and identity.

It invites a collective understanding of how ill people make sense of key life experiences and what it means to them, helping to narrow the gap between medical science and the human experience.

I would like to use my art to overcome the 'invisibility' that is often associated with illness so that people can 'see' what illness looks like and how it feels and that people with illnesses have a voice, can be creative and need to be seen. Above all, I want to open dialogues and create agency with regard to facilitating expressions of illness. Dividing my time between Manchester in the UK and Colombo in Sri Lanka, I hope to generate a wider awareness around this subject among patients, carers, health professionals and the general public.

Take a Bow, 2016

'Let's take a closer look at our creative space! See yourself through art. Be inspired. Be visible. Be heard.'

What I'd like to focus on

Creative expression has undeniable sustainable power. There is something about creativity, how we engage with it and share it with others, that influences our health. Using art to find meaning in what I am going through, and find purpose in sharing this experience with others, is somewhat empowering and helps me to cope and also **empower** myself by producing self-directed creations when the majority of the time the illness is trying to disempower me.

   Art helped me to **evolve** into someone new. My artistic expressions highlight underestimated, unrecognised burdens associated with an everyday way of life. It reveals the hidden realities of what the **essence** of being a patient looks like with long-term illness. Making the invisible visible, art gives me a visual voice trying to produce a bigger picture of the understated, poorly understood and misunderstood burdens associated with long-term illness. My art represents social inclusion and the mutual respect of people subjected to stereotyping and stigma due to illness or disability. The profound psychosocial impact of illness makes it a challenging

Depth of My Eye, 2016
My digital canvases aim to capture the essence of being a patient, the many shades of my everyday life with vasculitis.

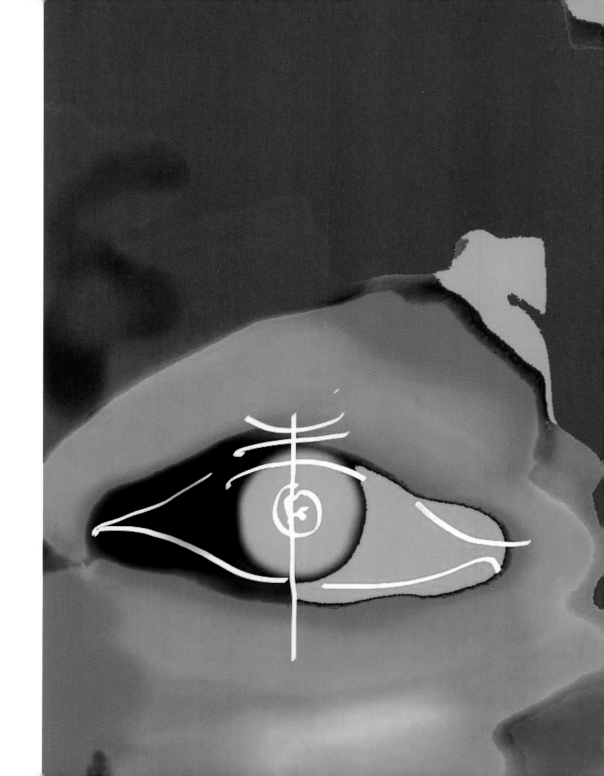

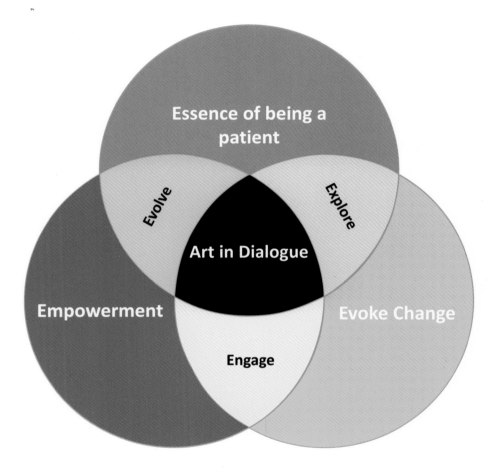

experience. Art is an outlet, a form of healing that helps to portray the subjective experience of illness. Art can act as a visual language to shift perception and break communication barriers in healthcare encounters and can add sensory dimensions to improve patient-clinician conversations.

Art has the capacity to **engage** the community and aid social transformation, a platform that can **evoke** change. Art encourages self-reflection, looking inwards at the way we see and think. Given the opportunity, art can influence, inspire and enable individual as well as collective change by helping us get better at seeing more of the face behind the illness, and not just the person with an illness. My concept of 'creative empowerment **explores** the healing power of art' aims to engage with the community to see beyond illness or disability. It should bring the self into focus, refuting the idea that illness should define who we are. There is power in social engagement, cultural inclusion and mutual respect generated through art.

I hope my digital artwork is able to show this and generate awareness around this topic.

Part One: Essence
Vasculitis and Me

Step inside my inner reality, up
close and personal with illness.

'Life isn't about waiting for the storm to pass ...
It's about learning to dance in the rain.'

Vivian Greene

How do you see me?

Art has helped me to redefine myself after illness distorted my identity and image. I am using my story as a starting point and the personally resonant images in this book to explore the role art played to transform my illness experience. Making the 'invisible visible', my visual narrative of struggle, acceptance and adaptation made over time looks at how vulnerability and isolation affect us when we go through challenging situations. Starting conversations, narratives in art form, if you will, my dialogue begins.

The images that follow express and illustrate my personal attempts to deal with my illness. I have offered explanations and interpretations for some of the works; others I leave to your imagination. What do you see? What do you want to see? What do you feel when you see them?

What my artworks mean to me and how I decipher them is entirely personal, a modification of my perceptions. They may carry a different meaning for you. You may see what I see in a parallel or contrasting way, and you may also see something additional to what I describe. Even though I would very much like you to notice what I observe in my images, I encourage you to apply your own observations and thoughts. Take a moment to pause, dwell on what's in front of you. Step inside the image to explore the depths within, moving past the outer layer of the drawing. I have also included some of my poems and thoughts alongside several of the images to show how one creative impulse can spark another and how we should be open to any form of self-expression, no matter how it manifests itself. The important thing is to open your mind and give yourself the freedom to say what you want to say – by any means necessary, using any form of expression.

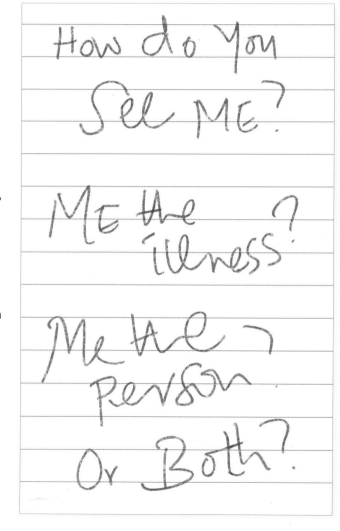

How do I see me?
How do you see me?
Me, the illness?
Me, the person?
Or both?

Do you see the face behind the illness?

Opposite: *Life Stills*, 2017

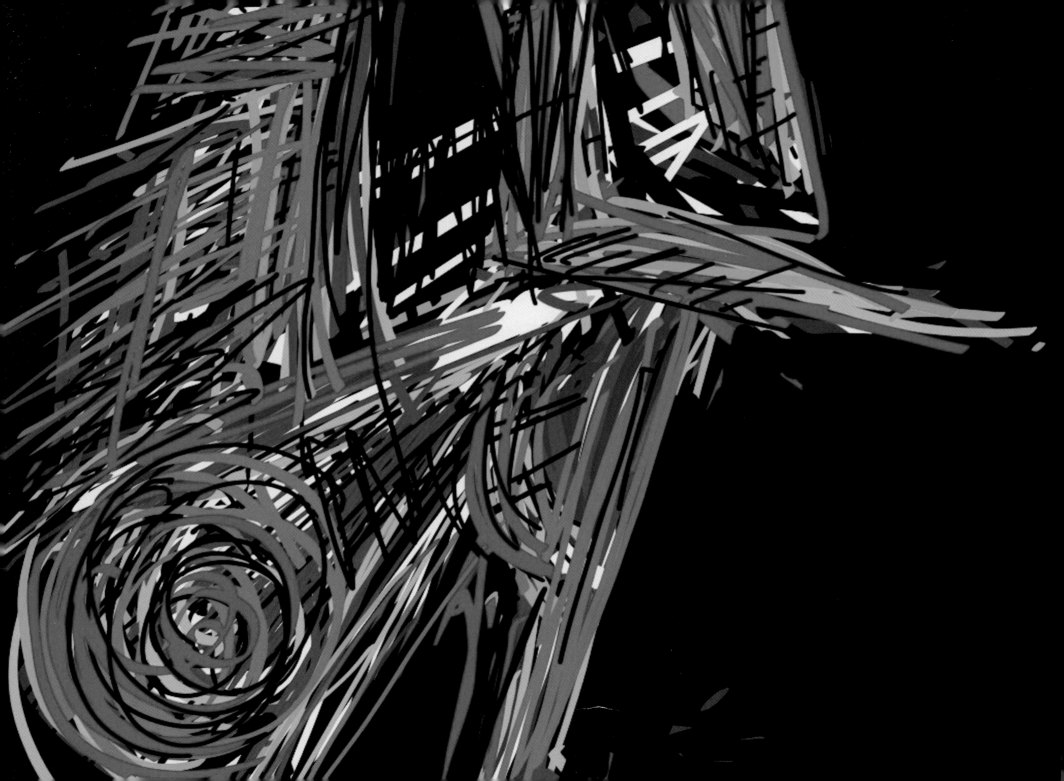

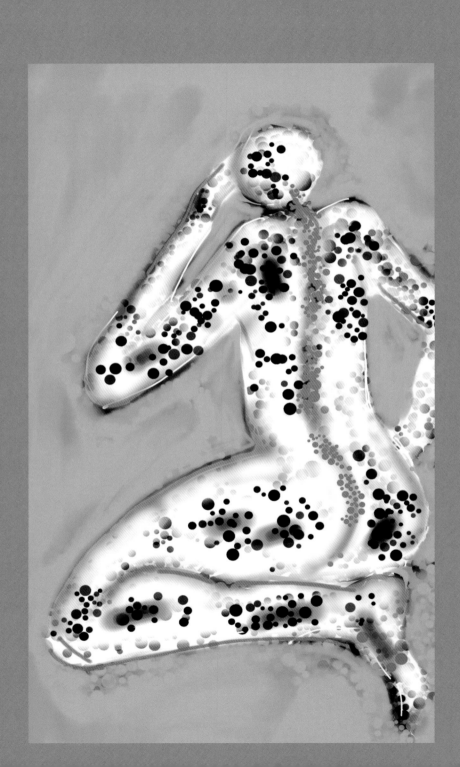

Vasculitis and Me
The struggle
The uncertainty
Loss of control
Battling beasts within

My inner reality

Finding symmetry within asymmetric inner chaos:
What I mean by symmetry is the ability to retain balance, to maintain physiological and emotional equilibrium from within. Asymmetry is formed by the disruptive force of chaos brought on by the illness, threatening this balance and equilibrium.

Making the invisible visible:
Using creative expression to divulge and communicate what goes on 'backstage' in my hidden inner world.

Opening dialogues:
'Do you see the face behind the illness?' The person with their strengths, and not just the person with the illness. The person trying hard to fit the norm in spite of their pain and suffering.

Opposite: *Vasculitis & Me*, 2018
I use colour to portray the different energies that drive inflammation and the battles within my body.
Right: *Stolen Moments*, 2020

43

Right: *Layers Within*, 2017
The struggle: impact of life on illness versus illness on life.

Opposite: *Stolen Moments*, 2016
I am exploring perceptions of my identity with lines, shapes and mixing different colours. Bringing the self into focus, I found the opportunity to reflect on how illnesses can start to define who we are.

Stolen Moments

'I face life
The storm
The calm
The in–between
Living each day'

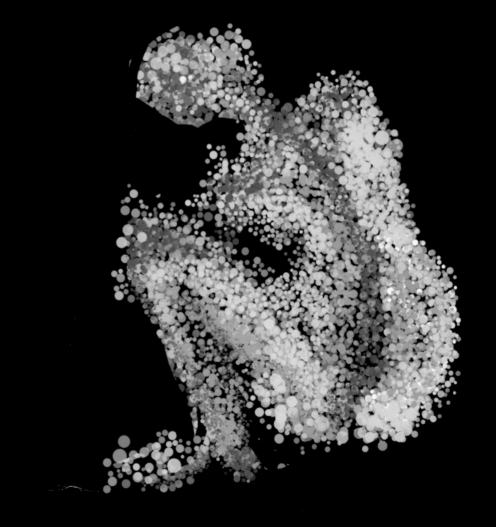

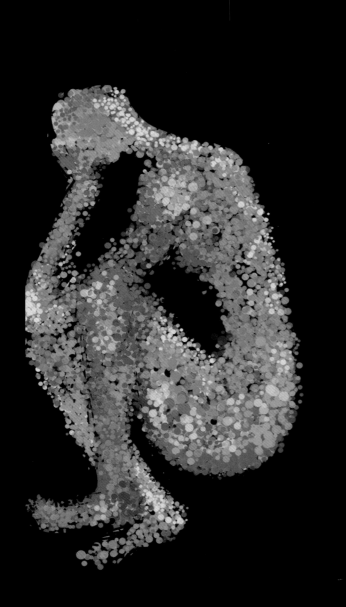

Stolen Moments

'I walk past
Life's stolen moments
Shadows that haunt
Of shattered dreams
Glimpsing reflections
Of who I was'

Right: *Stolen Moments,* 2016
Opposite: *Stolen Moments – When Skies Are Grey,* 2016
Stolen moments: robbed of dreams and life expectations.

Left: *Interconnections*, 2020
Opposite left: *Powerless*, 2015
Opposite right: *Fatigue*, 2015

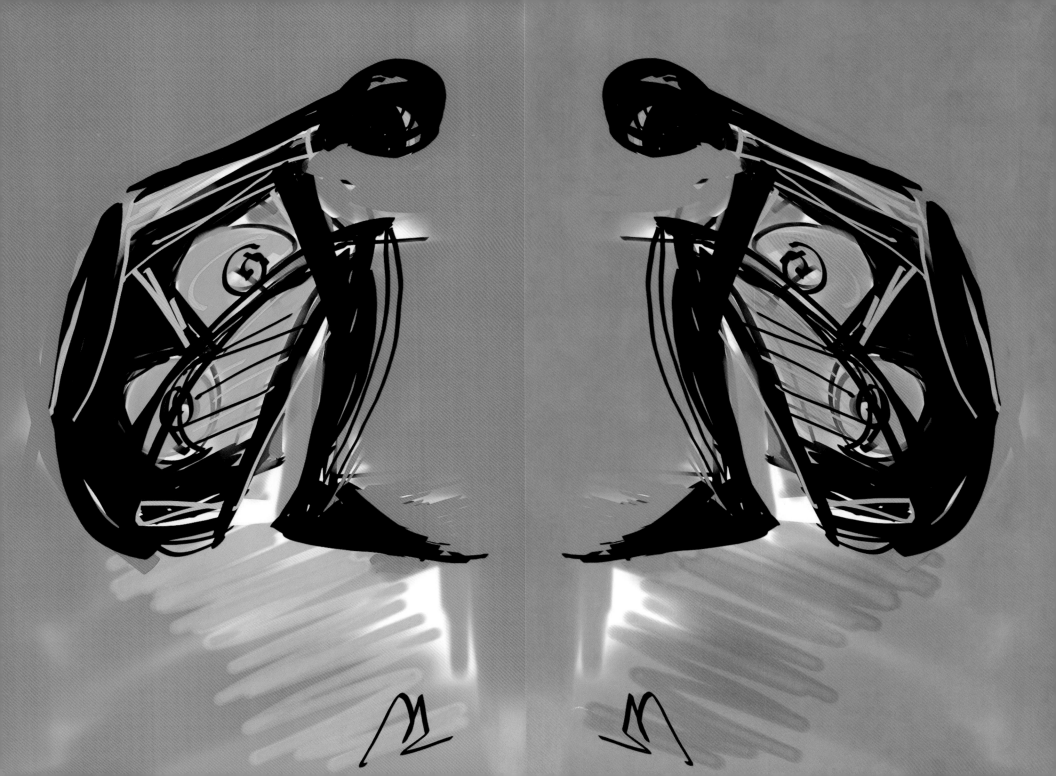

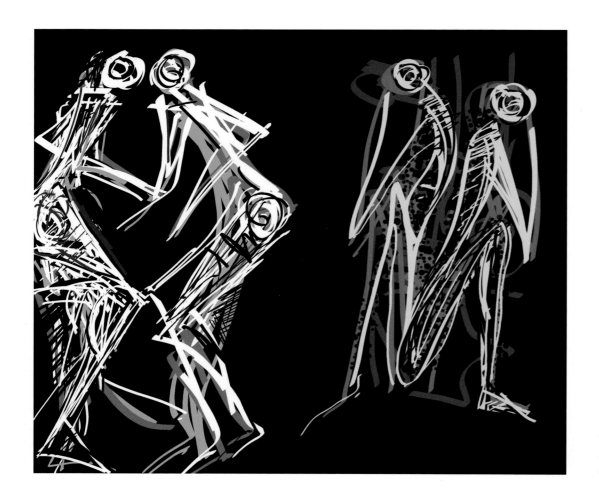

Left: *Fracture*, **2019** A sense of dislocation from myself. The ravages of the illness often bring on a state of powerlessness, fracturing the natural flow of life. A split within the self.
Opposite: *Life Stills*, **2017**

Life Stills

I keep stumbling
I keep falling
I keep breaking
I struggle to get back up

I fall back
I can't keep up
I am left behind

Time passes
I try to get back up
I try to keep up
I feel stagnant
I feel still

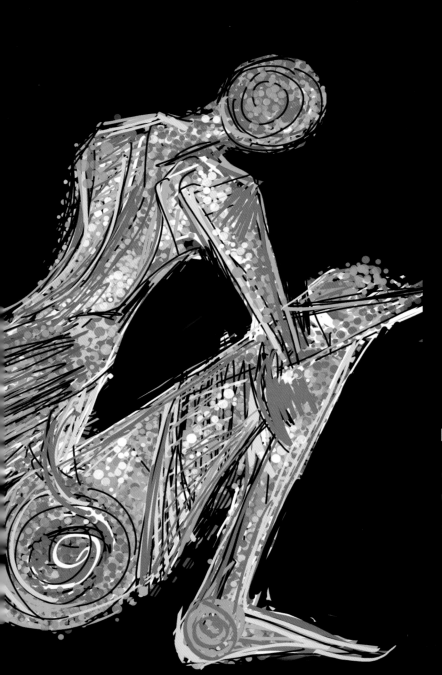

Battles Within

I lose sight
I lose control
I lose me

Opposite: *Life Stills,* 2017
Battle with loss of self-identity and upholding standards. Role reversal from doctor to patient. Loss of career.

Right: *Stuck in the Mud,* 2019
Illnesses have the capacity to take on a life of their own. I felt as though I was stuck in the mud, overtaken by a new force. At times, unable to move forward.

Left and opposite: *Inner Turmoil*, **2017**
Feeling trapped by restrictions imposed on
myself and my lifestyle by illness. Battle with
image distortion and loss of self-identity.

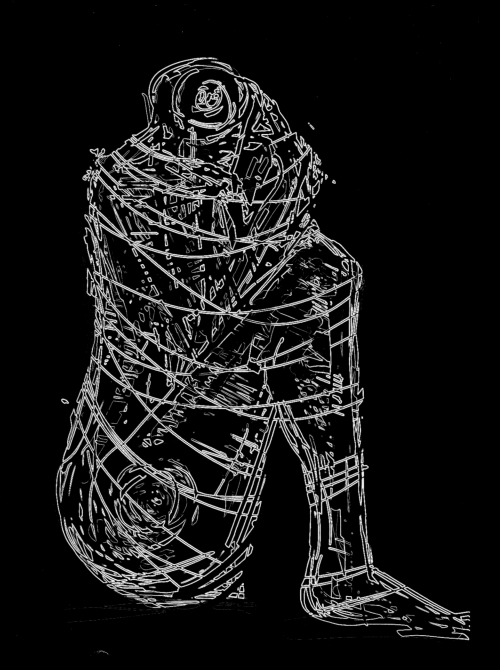

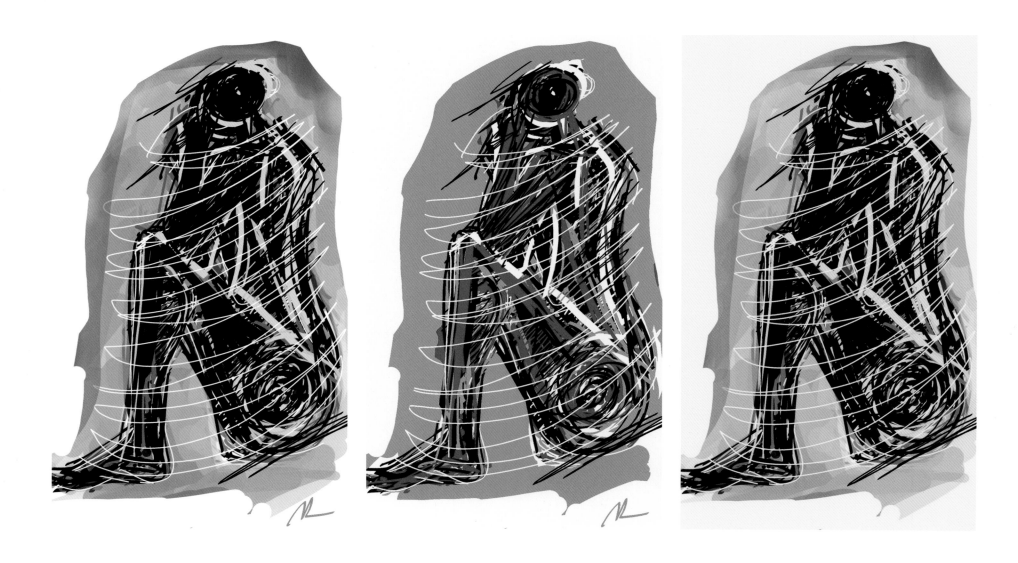

Layers Within, **2017** Varying shades depicting the spectrum of emotions, from feeling overwhelmed to angry and agitated, to apprehensive and uncertain.

Layers Within, 2016 Exposed to physical, emotional, spiritual, social and cultural elements at once.

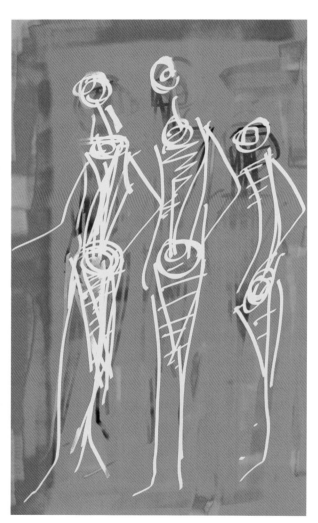

***Subjected to Social Pressures*, 2017–2018** I felt I could not keep up with my friends, peers and everyone around me. I felt left behind and subjected to all sorts of social expectations and pressures. I felt vulnerable and isolated.

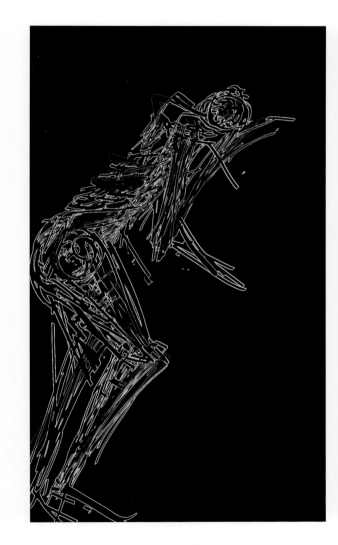 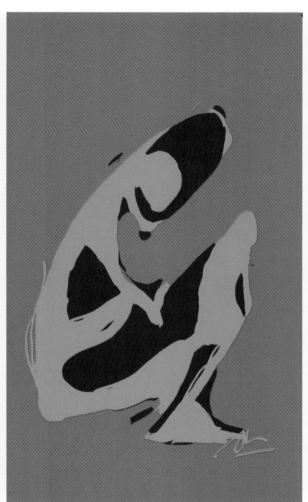 

Humanity, 2017, 2017 and 2019

 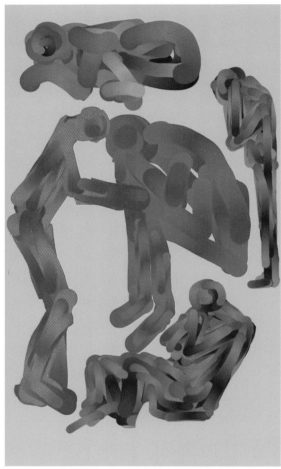 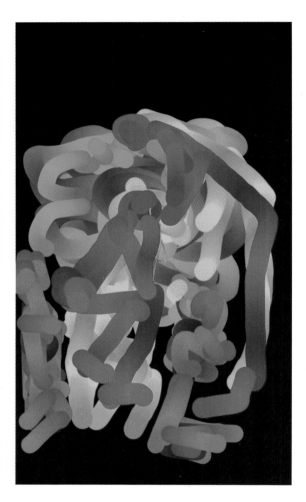

Humanity, 2016, 2015 and 2015

***Vulnerability and the Long-term Illness,* 2018**
Long-term illnesses and health challenges force us to confront and think
about vulnerability and life in new ways. Feeling powerless and the loss of
control, low self-esteem and low self-confidence made me feel vulnerable.

Isolation #1

Isolation, who am I?

I walk with you hand in hand at times,
I am there when you feel,
left out
helpless
unable to keep up
not in control
out of place, not fitting in

I can be there when you are with others
I can be there when you are alone
I am there at times of despair

You see me always as 'doom and gloom'
You can make use of me
I am not always dark
See the light in me

Use me to see within you

Isolation #2

Isolation,
how do you see me?

You see me mostly as a 'sinking ship'
You see me as cheerless 'kinship'

I am submerged, during life's hustle, bustle and rustle
The moment life stills and quiet sets in
The moment you are forced to pause and slow down
The moment you are stripped from routine,
I emerge

I know 'on the whole' you see,
Inspiration
Imagination
Insight
Ideas, as positive drives
Why can you not see me, as one?

You mostly see me as the drive
to make you mope, downbeat
Sometimes even to make you cry

Help me to make you upbeat
Help me to make you smile

See me beyond the gloom
See me beyond the moment
See me in the light

Isolation, 2020

Above: *Isolation*, 2019
Opposite: *Pain, Isolation, Despair and Vulnerability*, 2016–2018
Art can be a visual language to express a broad range of
emotions, pain and fatigue; putting them into colours or shapes
by sketching or doodling can help to take the focus away from
them and help manage them better on a day-to-day basis.

Finding Me Beyond Illness

 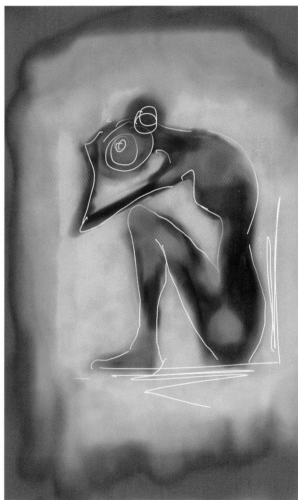 

Above: *I Am Fire*, **2016–2018** Tongues of fire: during a flare, the whole body feels as though it's on fire. This is what pain looks like to me.
Opposite: *The Pain That Burns Within*, **2016**

66

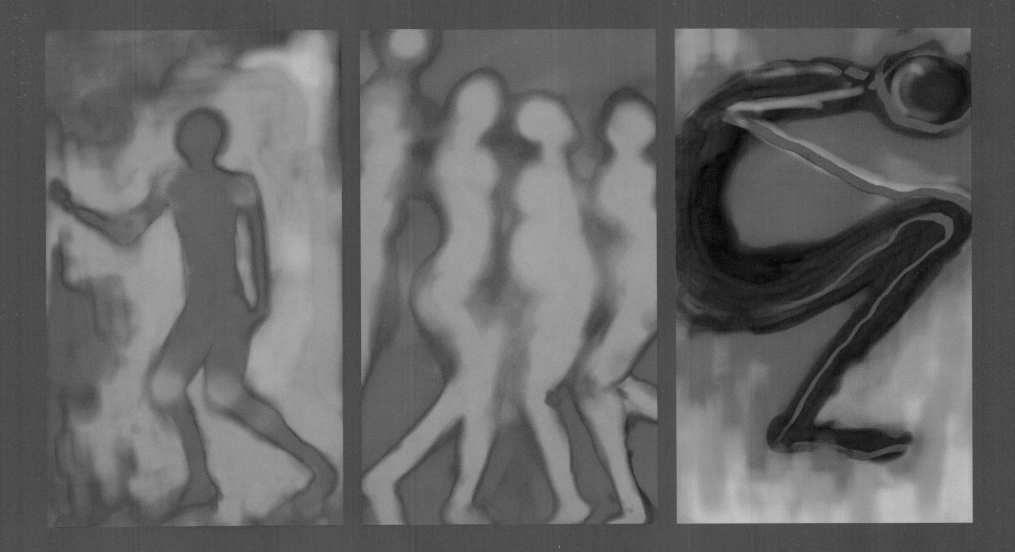

Part Two: Evolve
Finding the New Me

'Art washes away from the soul
the dust of everyday life.'

Pablo Picasso

Opposite: *The Pain That Burns Within, 2016–2018*

Transcending illness: how did I incorporate art into healing and self-management?

Art played a big part in transforming my illness narrative. I used art as a tool to:

1. Regain control

The act of making art allowed me to be in control of directing and shaping my drawing. Engaging in this creative activity gave me a sense of achievement. This helped me to focus on what I can do in defiance of the pain, tingling, numbness and fatigue I experience with repeated use of my hands. It felt I was taking back control from something that stole control from me, reclaiming power over areas dominated by the illness. It was my first step towards regaining a sense of control and navigating my journey in a forwards direction. It involved adapting to a newer lifestyle.

2. Cope

Creating art helped to take the focus away, even for a few minutes, from ongoing symptoms like pins and needles, and the tingling and sharp jolts I experience in my hands, arms, feet and legs; severe transient stabbing pains in my face and eyes; a feeling like hot and cold water running down my face; and areas along my legs that feel like a raw wound. Art helps me bear what's going on. The distraction art creates helps me to cope better with fatigue, which is one of my limiting symptoms. There are 'battery recharging' days where I stay in bed all day, recovering from severe fatigue, especially if I've done something extra the day before. I call myself a 'fatigue being'. There is no medication to treat fatigue, and I find drawing is a useful tool to deal with it.

3. Communicate

Art provides a visual language to communicate what I am going through when I can't find the words to describe it; at the same time it also propagates a richer awareness of my unseen inner world. Being able to construct the concept and process visually helped me to better accept the changes brought on by my illness, showing me ways to elaborate, expose and communicate the experience to myself and others.

'Life is not a matter of holding good cards, but of playing a poor hand well.'

Robert Louis Stevenson

1. Regain control

Chronic diseases can turn lives upside down, gradually changing the landscape of daily living. That's what happened to me. The illness tried to take over my life. Coping with the challenges of daily life is a complex task. Illness has a way of interrupting life, through pain, fatigue, new symptoms, side effects from drugs, flare-ups of underlying symptoms and mood swings. In addition, there are many understated emotional, cultural, social and political influences that govern us and that make the whole lived experience difficult to endure. Like most people going through similar situations, at first I couldn't comprehend that I would not be able to revisit my previous state of wellness, physical, social or emotional. And of course it led to me grieving for aspects of myself that couldn't be reclaimed.

I tried very hard to find a new baseline for myself, but with time I realised that my baseline would be dynamic, and I had to learn to adjust and adapt to fluctuations and changes. Health becomes a balance between coping, adapting and accepting versus the control of the disease, pain and your emotional state. Reality imposed by illness tends to define and redefine itself over time. Coping with change requires constant reorganising and self-redefinition. Accepting the realities of the illness, recognising the chronicity of symptoms and working with change was key to freeing myself from the grasp my illness had on me, my attitudes and my approach to life.

What does 'losing control' feel like in these situations?
What does constant change feel like?

'Creativity takes courage.'

Henri Matisse

Shifting sands

Adaptive coping with digital art helped me to create something visible, touchable, perceivable and this generated a sense of achievement, which in turn gave me more control and allowed me to regain my self-worth, to be more flexible with my time and efforts and be less of a perfectionist. This sense of achievement helped me to set more realistic and achievable goals.

This also led to the rediscovery of myself by seeing myself in a new role, the whole 'before and now' response to an altering shift in roles, priorities, perceptions and refocusing. Over time, I realised that enrolling the help of family and friends became a necessity, and it was not a sign of weakness to ask for help.

- Adaptations over time of attitude, image, identity and lifestyle

- Find new tools and ways around limitations

Right: *Shifting Sands*, **2017**
Opposite: *Adaptation*, **2019**

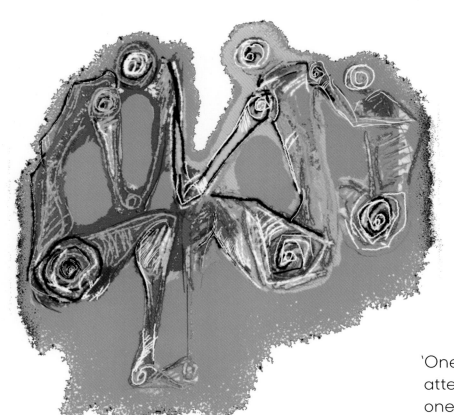

'One must from time to time
attempt things that are beyond
one's capacity.'

Pierre-Auguste Renoir

Altering perception

Changing the focus away from an illness that had taken control, art offered a route to escape the restrictions imposed by that illness on myself and my lifestyle.

For me, seeing myself through art was an inner sanctuary, helping me to confront reality with its continuing changes.

Reassessing, reprioritising and readjusting the tipping balance helped me to find my new identity and regain self-worth.

This transition was the core to my rebuilding confidence and progressing forwards.

'Normality is a paved road. It's comfortable to walk, but no flowers grow on it.'

Vincent Van Gogh

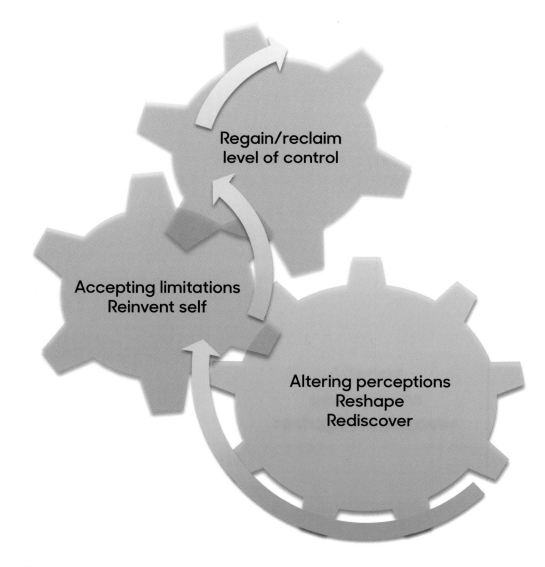

Transition to adaptive coping > Counter change > Game changer

Accepting limitations

Part of coping with the illness was about learning to accept my new circumstances and understanding the limitations I would face in my new reality. It's a process I needed to work through based on being aware of what will change and what the impact of those changes will be for me. It was hard work, and I had to keep reaccessing what worked best for me at the time and modify my lifestyle accordingly. I had to reconstruct my day and activities to conserve energy for the essential tasks at hand.

'We are stronger in the places we have been broken.'

Ernest Hemingway

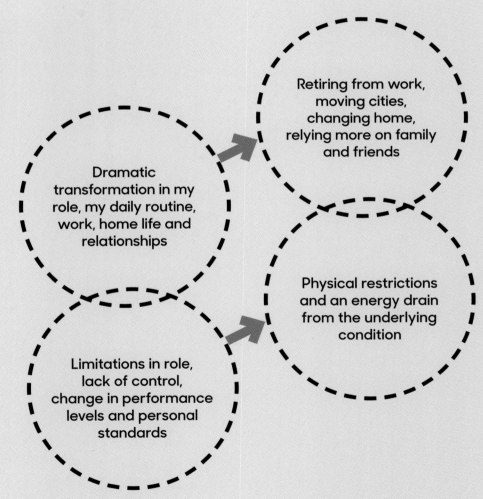

Learning to accept, adjust and adapt to the shifts in role and routine

Illness makes you a different person: 'who you were' has now transformed into 'who you have become', a new person with an added personality: the illness. Holding on to whom you were before is not only impossible it is limiting. If you don't accept this and reject this different person, you become stuck in a tiresome and lonesome repetitive cycle, stagnating in one place. Whether you like it or not, you are not the same person.

Greek Philosopher Heraclitus (535–475 BC) said, 'No man ever steps in the same river twice, for it's not the same river and he's not the same man'. He describes that everything around us and within us undergoes a consistent process of change, reminding us of the notion that change is the only constant in our universe. He goes to on say that 'All is flux, nothing stays still'. Everything moves and everything changes.

It was very frustrating at first, but I had to embrace the different person I had become. This was the key to moving on. It meant revising my priorities in life – what's really important to me now? – shifting my role, as a worker, friend and family member: accommodating myself to a new lifestyle and accepting the limitations of my altered existence. The two images here show the acceptance of the handover – the body positions and the posture remain the same, but the different colour filters represent the emotional dynamics involved, the shifts in energies as change transpires as part of my reshaping. I try to show the stark contrast, akin to night becoming day and day becoming night. My role changed from doctor to someone in between: doctor, patient, artist and educator.

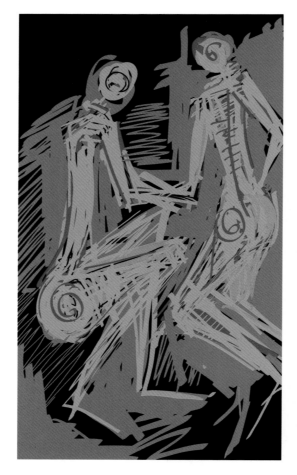

Reshaping My Lifestyle, 2017

'If you can't fly, then run. If you can't run, then walk. If you can't walk, then crawl. But whatever you do, you have to keep moving forward.'

Martin Luther King Jr.

Beyond the Shadow of Illness, 2019

You can't control your day or your illness, but you can control what you create

Creativity is a means of taking control of and constructing a positive identity. It became clear to me that the art of getting on top of the situation was to regain control and self-respect. Reclaiming myself from overpowering emotions and the dominating illness became a significant component in managing my condition and moving forward with my life. From my experience, adapting to find ways around limitations played a central role in rebuilding my confidence and looking ahead.

Art is boundless, unconditional. Art transcends time, space, pain and illness. Similarly, our imagination is limitless. This enables us to create as well as appreciate the meaning, beauty and abstraction of art. This way, art can become a valuable resource to handle sudden changes going from familiar terrain to new, unfamiliar territory.

I used the creative space to reflect and adapt, working around my limitations.

Creative energy helped me to discover myself through self-expression and explore the depths within, the resilience, the inner courage. The artistic experience allowed me to express and symbolise feelings about the illness as a whole-person involvement, engaging the heart, mind and emotions.

Art helped me to see myself in a different light, to realise there is purpose and meaning beyond the limitations imposed by my illness. I found myself tapping into aspects of me I didn't know existed. By redefining, reexamining and reconstructing aspects of the 'new me', I found someone new.

Adaptations over time, like shifting sands moulding sandcastles, made me alter perspective by seeing myself in a new role.

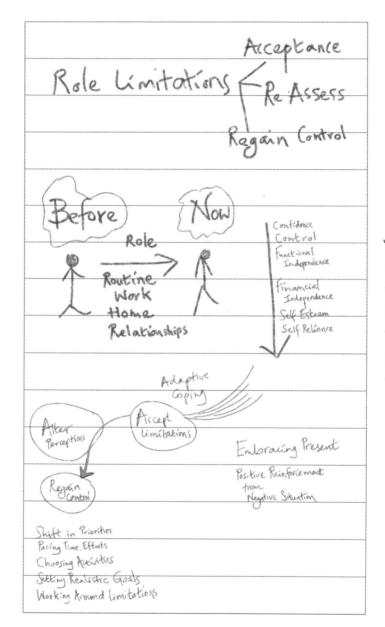

'Creative expression through art can be a way for transcending pain, illness and disability.'

Rebranding and rediscovering self-identity

Art has helped me to redefine aspects of the 'new me' after illness dominance distorted my identity and image.

It has helped me learn how to walk past old expectations and personal standards that had been set for my 'pre-illness' self.

Transcending my illness through art helped me to defy being defined by my illness.

I managed to transform the role reversal from doctor to patient back to a new role of artist and educator.

'Life isn't about
finding yourself.
Life is about
creating yourself.'
George Bernard Shaw

I Am Me, 2017

Becoming someone new...

What defines me?

Is it what I do?

Is it what I stand for?

Is it what I believe in?

How are my image and identity perceived?

What was then **vs** What is now

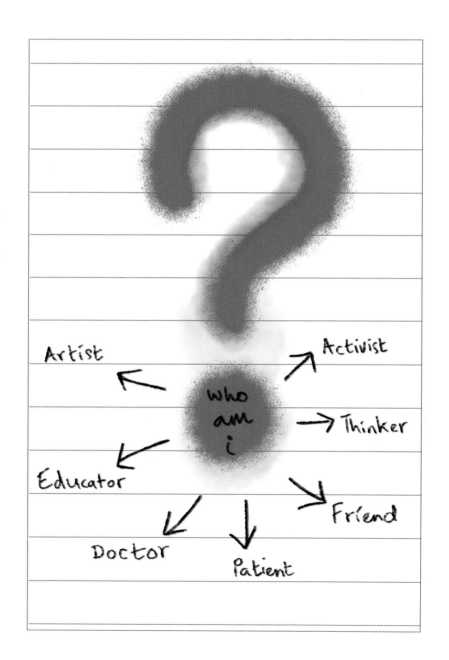

Defining Me

I stumble
I fall
I break
I mend
I get back up

I keep stumbling
I keep falling
I keep breaking
I struggle to get back up
I listen…

I feel pain
I burn
I weep
I scream
I listen…

I lose sight
I lose control
I lose me

I ask myself
Who I
Want me to be?
Need me to be?
Make me to be?

I struggle
I adapt
I alter
I shift
I cope
I listen

I define me
I defy being defined by illness

I the author
I the architect
I the enforcer of my life journey
Define me

I find me again

I see me now
Do you see me?

I Am Me, 2017

I Am Me, 2017

***Waves of Transitions*, 2018** Adaptations through phases over time to self-image, attitude and lifestyle.

Acceptance and Recovery, 2016–2018
The 'once was' setting of daily living reshaped.

2. Cope

Illness can overtake life at times. For me, art was a way to tap into my reservoir of resilience to face the uncertainty of illness. Tackling constant challenges forced me to revisit coping strategies that worked for me until I found one that offered the best quality of life possible.

Art was my strategy, and it played a part in:

- Being a refuge from the sudden changes in routine and the dynamic shifts in my role
- Managing everyday symptoms like pain and fatigue by shifting my focus
- Building endurance to handle:

  Emotions and mood swings, anger and frustration

  Stress

  The daily challenges of dealing with functional limitations

'I am still learning.'

Michelangelo

Coping with the Illness Experience, **2018**
Taking focus away from pain and fatigue is a great distraction.

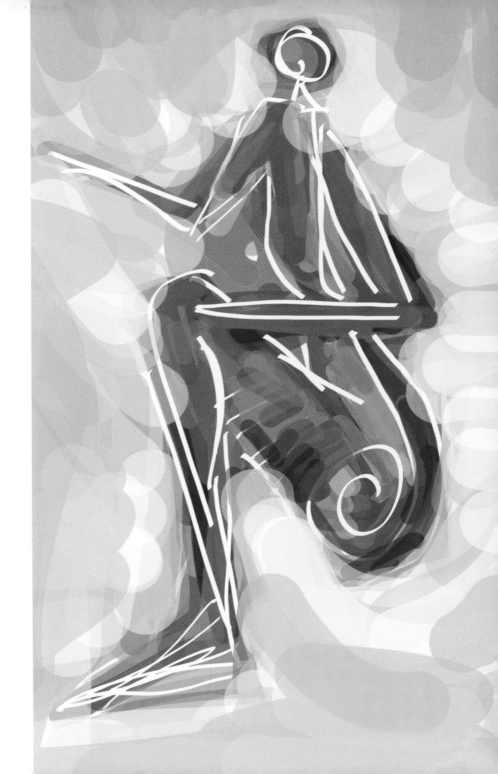

Left: *Introspection*, 2019
Opposite: *Enduringness*, 2016

Building endurance
to deal with
daily challenges
and emotions.

Variants, 2019
The multiple shades of everyday living with illness,
depicting the uncertainty and sudden variations
in emotions and symptoms.

The Essence of Being Me, **2019**
Taming the beasts within. Adjusting and
reshaping image and identity over time.

The Essence of Being Me, 2019
These three variants of the same image show the different stages of my illness progression, first in my feet and legs and extending to the back of my lower limbs, then my hands. It then moved to my brain and affected the nerves supplying my face.

The two figures are both me: the one on the left is the me developing the illness and the one on the right side is the me trying to deal with all the changes.

The bent head and stooping posture represents feeling beaten and succumbing to illness. The spiral shapes over the hips show interruption and the hardships encountered with mobility.

Shifting DYNAMICS, 2019

Pause. Take a moment to reflect on the images in front of you. You may see movement and some activity. You may wonder what's going on here.

The first three images in the row above show the stepwise rise to achieving a better level of coping with daily challenges, illustrated by the posture and positional change of the figures. Here again, the two figures are both me. The illness self and the other self. The joining of hands at the top is about the growing strength and acceptance of both halves of me. Joining forces to unite as one. The different colour filters demonstrate the dynamics in emotional energy and mood, shifting from calm to chaos, to somewhere in between. The wave patterns indicate the flow of responsiveness to the happenings in my life and the day-to-day variability – like shifting sands, moving from one state to another.

The remaining two images in the row above are part of the same journey. Here, beside my two selves, seen more in harmony with each other, are other figures too. It shows as time goes by how I began to see my interactions with the outside world and how the outside world sees me.

It is important to note that the illness self and my other self are united as one, which implies I am in control and coping. This certainly helps others to see my 'whole self'.

Getting through the day: finding symmetry within asymmetry

I will ask you to pause again. Enter the images to see what's happening inside, and consider the different filters to see whether the variants of the same image can make you see the flexibility in mood.

The change in the colour filters represents the inner-body and out-of-body experience of resilience. Developing resilience to illness is part of taking action to cope with the disruptions it brings. This helps me to maintain balance within to get through the day. The lighter and darker backgrounds denote day and night, highlighting the variability in mood over each 24-hour period.

The symmetry I refer to is finding this balance, and the asymmetry is the chaos within me. I am the figure seated on the left, and the other figures are interactions with friends, family and others I come across as a patient in health environments or as an educator in patient-support settings or medical student-teaching environments.

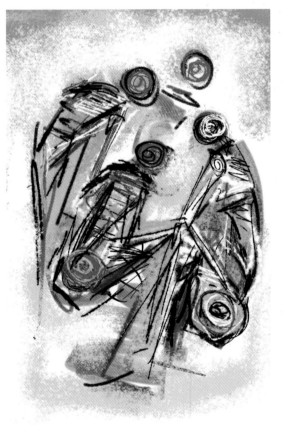

Above and opposite: *Getting through the Day,* 2019

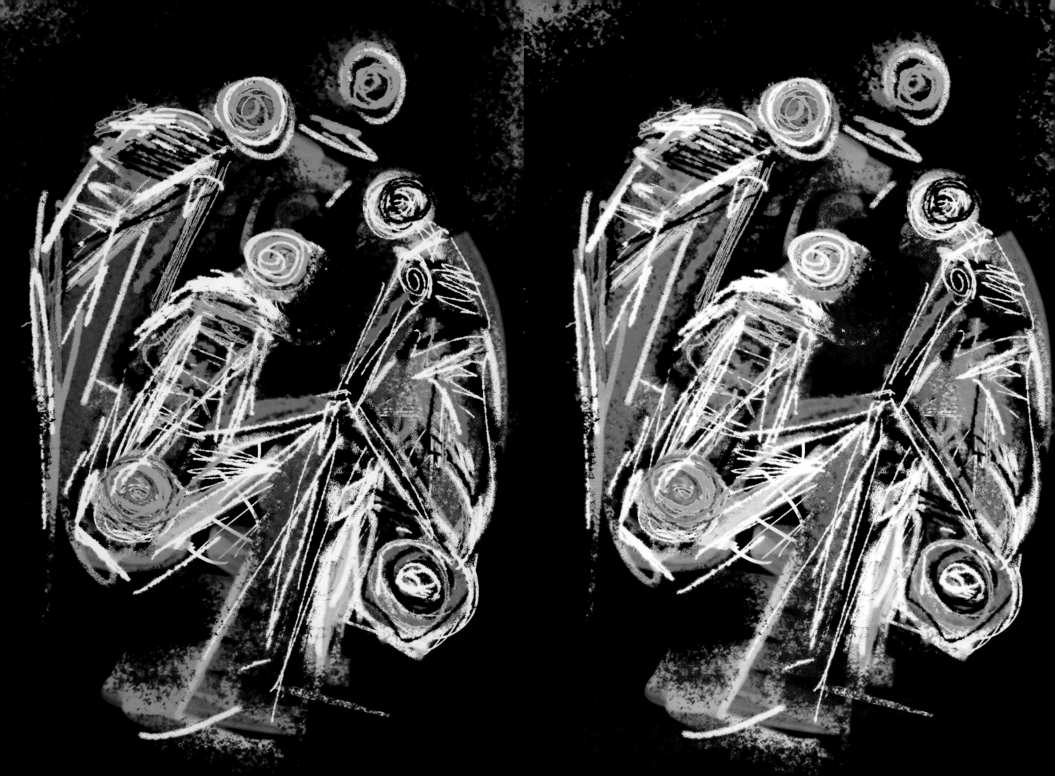

3. Communicate

I use art to illustrate my everyday living with illness in an attempt to objectify the subjective experience. Art can demonstrate a broad range of emotions the many facets of emotions and degrees of pain one goes through at various points in time. Art can be an effective nonverbal mode to communicate and connect with family, friends and health providers.

'A picture is a poem without words.'

Horace

Opposite and right: *Support,* 2020

Dialogue

Sharing art and personal reflections contributes to forming interpersonal connections, and this form of social learning generates a sense of achievement and increases self-worth, strengthening the inner connection.

Outer dialogue – connecting with others

Sharing this visual language of expression helps others gain newer insights and perspectives into what it is like to live with a long-term illness. A better understanding of emotions helps us to empathise with what's actually going on in the lives of people living with these conditions; it paves the way to a better appreciation of the 'portrait of illness'.

A visual demonstration of pain and vulnerability is a powerful tool for gaining insights into the physical, spiritual and emotional elements of the illness experience. It examines sociopolitical, religious and cultural issues influencing personal beliefs. It can also highlight the underestimated and ignored burdens associated with long-term illness, health challenges, disabilities and emotional trauma.

Inner dialogue – connecting with myself

For me, being able to put a variety of emotions, feelings, thoughts, pain, vulnerability and frustration into colour and shape helps me to document the impact illness has on me and my lifestyle. It's a journal or a colourful diary of my personal narrative.

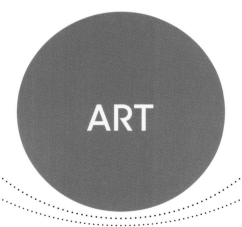

Outer Dialogue
Connecting with others

Inner Dialogue
Connecting with myself

ART

Synergy

In the intersection of the old me and the new me, I'm trying to find a balance, to take some of the positives from 'before' into the 'after', and create a synergy that builds on the past, looks to the future and acknowledges and incorporates the change that's taken place in order to get there.

I am able to liberate emotional energies that express frustration, pain and change by communicating them through art. It illustrates the inner dialogue I have with myself and the outer dialogue I have with others; it represents the inner- and out-of-body experience with my illness journey. Synergy is part of supporting this balance between my inner dialogue and my outer dialogue.

Achieving synergy involved integrating my illness self and my old self to put them in sync so that I become someone new. The images on the pages that follow are part of the series 'Synergy', representing this dialogue and integration.

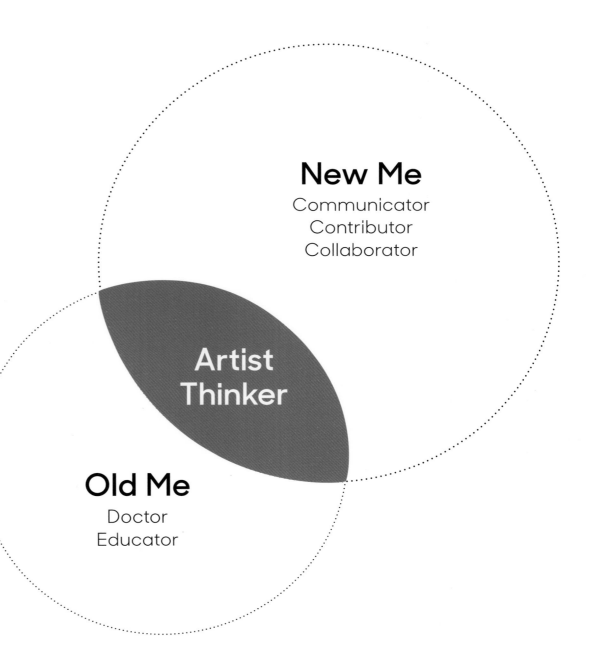

New Me
Communicator
Contributor
Collaborator

Artist
Thinker

Old Me
Doctor
Educator

 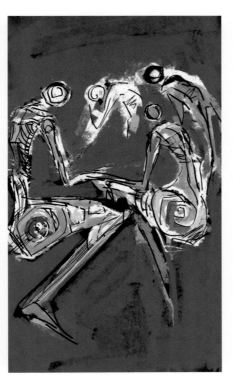  

Opposite and above: *Synergy,* **2016**
Harmony and resilience against the chaos of uncertainty and the uncertainty of chaos.

Left: *Synergy: Fighting to Maintain Harmony,* **2018** The macro and micro communications within myself and my outside environment. Working in unison to maintain balance despite surrounding chaos inside and outside.

Opposite: *Synergy,* **2019** Freeing up the energy that expresses anger, pain and frustration using different colours to show the variations in mood. The shapes show the ill-defined and haphazard nature of these feelings.

Above and opposite: *Synergy,* 2017

To be seen,
heard and included
gives more control
over day-to-day living.

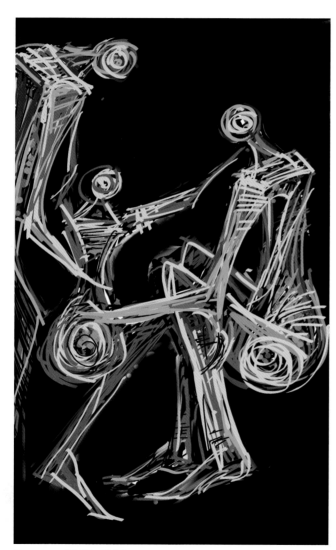

Synergy, 2017–2019

'I exist
I survive
I endure
I withstand
I meet life
I live'

Synergy, 2017

105

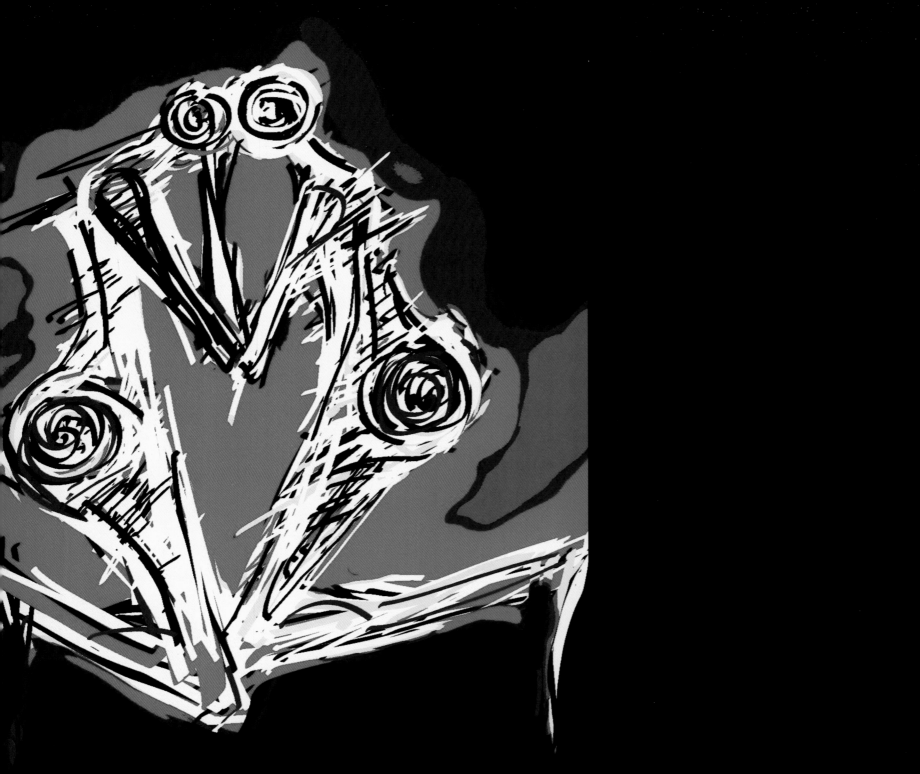

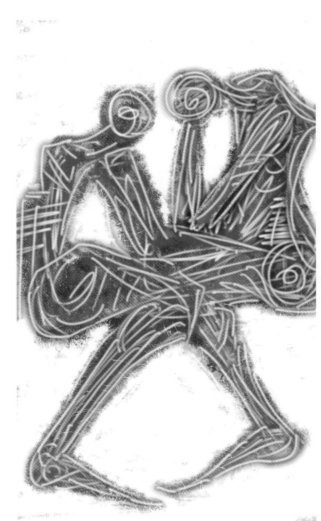

Opposite:
Synergy, 2017

Right: *Synergic Inter-representation Series 1,* **2018** Using art to see the true reality of illness, liberating the negative energies of pain, anger and frustration into more positive expressions, thereby restoring balance within me.

***Synergic Inter-representation Series 2**, 2017–2018*
The images in series 2 and 3 symbolise the connections
between me and my illness with another person experiencing
the same condition. It is the inter-representation of our illness
that creates a synergy between us.

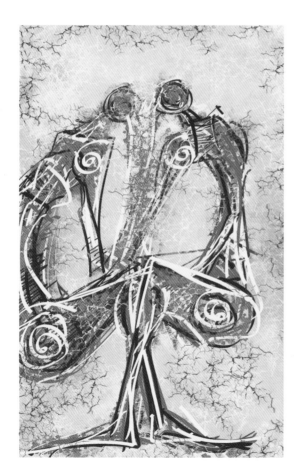

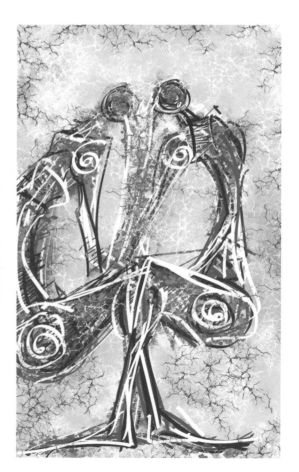

Synergic Inter-representation Series 3, 2017–2019

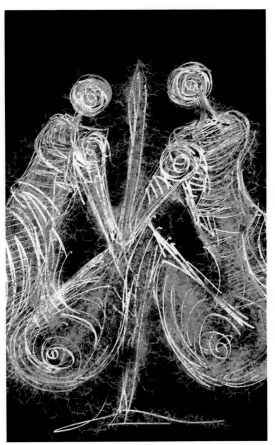
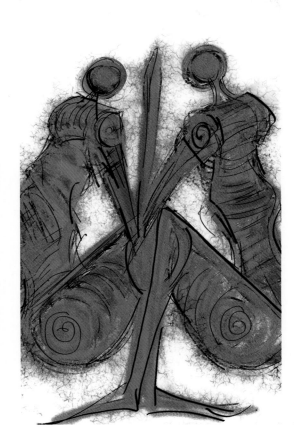

Living Each Day, 2019, 2017

Fluidity

I exist
I survive
I endure
I withstand
But most of all,

Living each day
I meet life
Life meets me
I dare to hope
Do you?

Fluidity, 2018

Above: *Connections*, **2019**
Connecting, contributing and sharing with others.

Opposite: *Connections*, **2019** I found that 'adaptive coping', with newer ways to work around my limitations, helped to transform my illness experience. Integrating creativity was my new way to cope, and it certainly aided my healing process. Communicating this with others can help to build connections as well as make people see beyond my illness.

Opposite: *Connection,* **2019** Connection is all about stepping out of your comfort zone to engage with friends, family and people around you.

Above: *Connecting amidst Chaos,* **2016, 2017 and 2018**

Flow

Nature at its natural rhythm swaying to the
beat of the rain and wind

Hurricanes, storms, gusty
winds and tsunamis come and go

So much movement, yet so calm
the natural order of balance
shifting, yet maintained

In the face of complex encounters
the flow continues …

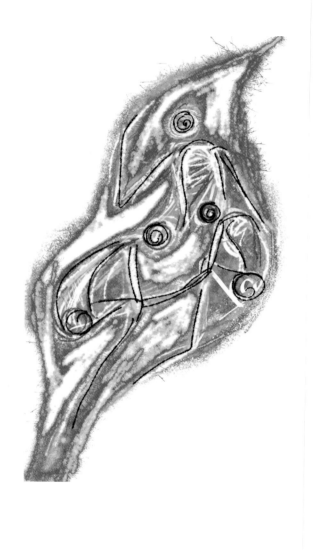

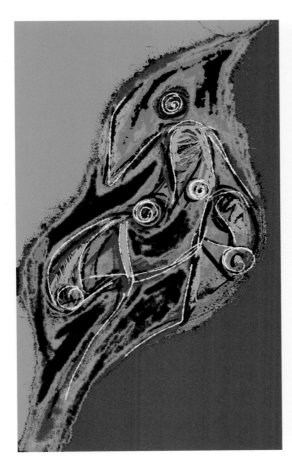 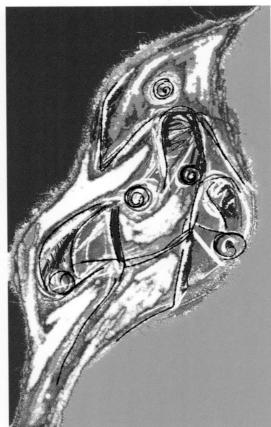 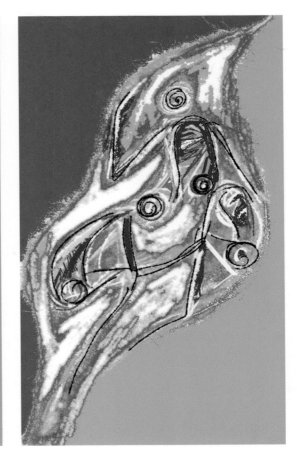

Above and opposite: *Flow*, 2019

Above and opposite: *Connections,* 2019

Part Three: Empower
In Sync with Me

'Art does not reproduce what we see.
It makes us see. One eye sees, the other feels.'

Paul Klee

Creative empowerment: Changing Lanes

The opportunity to dive into my creative side presented itself while I was recovering and adjusting to life with vasculitis. My journey with Changing Lanes began when I attended the British Society of Rheumatology Annual Conference in Glasgow, UK, in April 2016. I was invited to display some of my artwork at the patient event during the conference. This led to conversations with others in situations similar to mine as well as with health professionals about my experience of using creativity to transform the illness experience. A new chapter of my life began.

After losing myself in the illness, this was my first step towards reinventing my identity through creativity and art. The creative experience helped to express what I was feeling and going through from a deeper place of understanding: the somatic, attitudinal and social aspects of coping and living expressed through digital art.

From my experience, adapting to find ways around limitations played a key role in rebuilding confidence and progressing forwards. Even though a chronic illness disrupts a person's life, personal strength and perseverance can preserve the spirit. Even though the illness has brought about change and there are constant reminders of its presence, the central focus of my life, I now recognise, has to be on me as a person not solely governed by illness.

Self-discovery and the power of resilience

I used digital art to capture the anticipation of new symptoms or the worsening of those symptoms, the uncertainty of my illness trajectory and my emerging resilience when it came to regaining control of my mind and body.

In my darkest moments, the emerging 'face of resilience' against the chaos of uncertainty has helped me to maintain balance. Art provides a way to continuously reinforce my self-affirming capacity for resilience. Illustrating the inner- and out-of-body experience with my illness helps me to connect with myself, accept change and take charge, going to a better place away from the illness encounter.

Through my artwork, I aim to reflect on my personal experience to raise awareness on 'creative empowerment – exploring the healing power of art'. My personal insights as a clinician and a patient, integrating creativity, healing and health, are transformed through creative expression into a

Opposite: *Resilience*, 2018

'Art helped me to realize the full potential of the self within.'

tool I can use to face some of the physical limitations and challenges imposed by chronic illnesses.

I am keen to tell others of my experiences as they may benefit from incorporating art or similar creative expressions into their own healing. This helps me to find purpose and set more realistic and achievable goals as well as refocus and reprioritise my own roles in life.

There is more to my life than my 'disease'. My illness journey gave me the opportunity to gain considerable insight into myself and my lifestyle.

It became clear to me that the art of coping well is to regain control and self-respect. What we believe reinforces our reality. This alone was an empowering thought. Quality of life is governed by not only how we act, the way we feel or what we can do but also how we think.

State of relaxation, stress relief and spiritual renewal

Accepting the realities of the illness and regaining a sense of control, a sense of purpose becomes a significant component in managing my long-term condition. Having a tool, be it art, gardening or cooking, for example, on top of other medications and therapies, becomes very useful in helping to adjust to change and combat day-to-day battles. Drawing on my own experiences is so useful in tackling symptoms such as fatigue and pain; establishing a sense of purpose strengthens my endurance to confront the illness and inspires forwards movement with my work and lifestyle.

For me, recognising the chronicity of symptoms and realising there's purpose and meaning beyond the limitations imposed by illness were important milestones in my journey. Constant demands from the illness forced me to revisit coping strategies that worked for me. This was when I recognised that learning ways to take charge of areas that still had power over the illness generated a sense of well-being. It showed me that I can break free from the clutches the illness has on me and my approach to life. This involved exploring new areas that could aid this process and reinforce my self-esteem and confidence. Exploring new tools helped me to deal with the situation.

Reshaping, redefining and rediscovering who I was by seeing myself in a new role gave me a sense of achievement. It triggered a sense of relief and well-being through the recognition and acknowledgment of subconscious feelings. Being in the creative space, one can achieve a state of liberation from anxiety and stress. Tapping into creative space brought me positive reinforcement, reflective thinking, mindfulness and relaxation. Having strategies such as art to help cope allowed me the best quality of life possible in spite of my limitations.

'Art provides a way to continuously reinforce my self-affirming capacity for resilience.'

Opposite: *In Full Bloom*, 2019

Self-discovery

Art can be used as a powerful tool while adjusting to illness and pain, accompanying what medicine has to offer. Having identified art as my tool, we come to the question: Why do I use the digital medium to draw?

Using a digital application on my mobile phone has enabled me to create art with minimal physical effort. I experience less pain and fatigue through this medium than when using a paintbrush on canvas or charcoal on paper.

I am working towards conveying the impact using an app on my mobile phone to create art has had on transforming my lifestyle supporting me to take control and manage my rare long-term condition. Getting the opportunity to share this awareness and my experience with others in similar situations, I hope, will help people think about newer ways and similar tools to cope with their challenges, empowering them to better adapt to chronic illnesses and disrupted work-life balances. For people who have limitations in hand function and have difficulty with traditional methods of drawing, the digital medium may be something they can explore. It empowered me.

In this way, the creative process was both a tool for supporting my self-development and an end in itself for me.

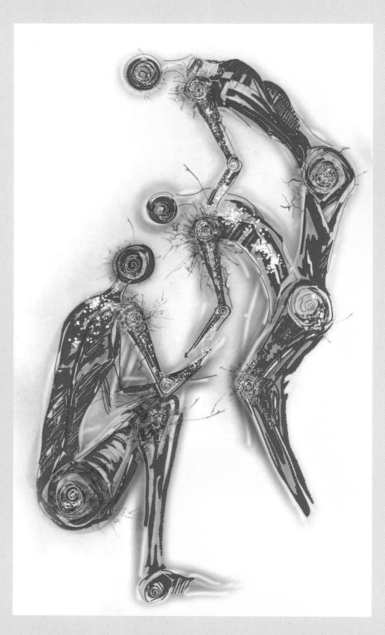

'I challenge illness dominance by using digital art.'

My Inner Reality, 2020

Self-esteem

The creation of a tangible piece of art can build confidence and nurture feelings of self-worth. Personal fulfilment comes from both the creative and reflective components of this process.

When it comes to a chronic illness, health becomes a balance between coping with, adapting to and adjusting around the various elements related to the disease.

Changing my personal attitudes towards illness was vital to looking ahead. The positive impact creative expression has on self-esteem and self-identity empowers me to maintain this balance. To feel I am back in charge of myself is empowering.

'Art can empower
and reshape lifestyles
to better adapt to
long-term illnesses.'

Fluidity, 2020

Face of courage

What is courage, I often wonder

What makes us strong?

What makes us weak?

We are both, at times

Waking up to face

Each day's unique battle

Keeping it together

Seeing beauty in unpleasantness

Despite challenges physical and emotional

None of us are immune to being human

Through moments of strength and weakness

I see it in us all

The face of courage

Resolution, 2017

***Creative Empowerment*, 2019** To use art to find meaning in
what I am going through, find purpose in sharing this experience
with others, and cope with the lived experience is empowering.
It certainly is empowering to be able to make self-directed
creations when, for the majority of the time, the illness is trying
to disempower me.

Self-discovery, 2017

Creative empowerment is achieved by:

- Self-exploration through art
- Learning to accept, adjust, adapt
- Taking focus away from illness
- Rediscovering the self by seeing myself in a new role
- Reassessing, reprioritising and refocusing my lifestyle
- Altering social perceptions, attitudes and cultural beliefs

Self-discovery through art – reshaping and redefining identity.

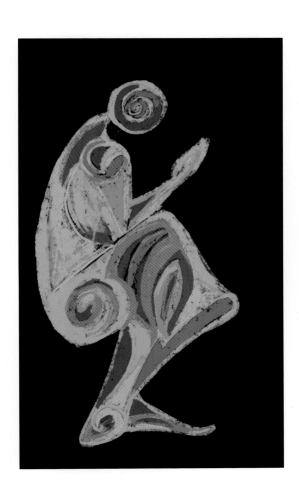

***Abstracts of Self*, 2019** These works bring 'me' into focus, reflecting on how illnesses can define who we are. They show different versions of me along my illness journey. Colour creates contrast, and the shapes, contours and lines portray the different energies surrounding me.

Above: *Do You See the Face Behind the Illness?*, 2019
The person with their strengths, not just the person with the illness.

Opposite: *I Am Me (Triptych)*, 2018
Focus on what I can do with my illness.

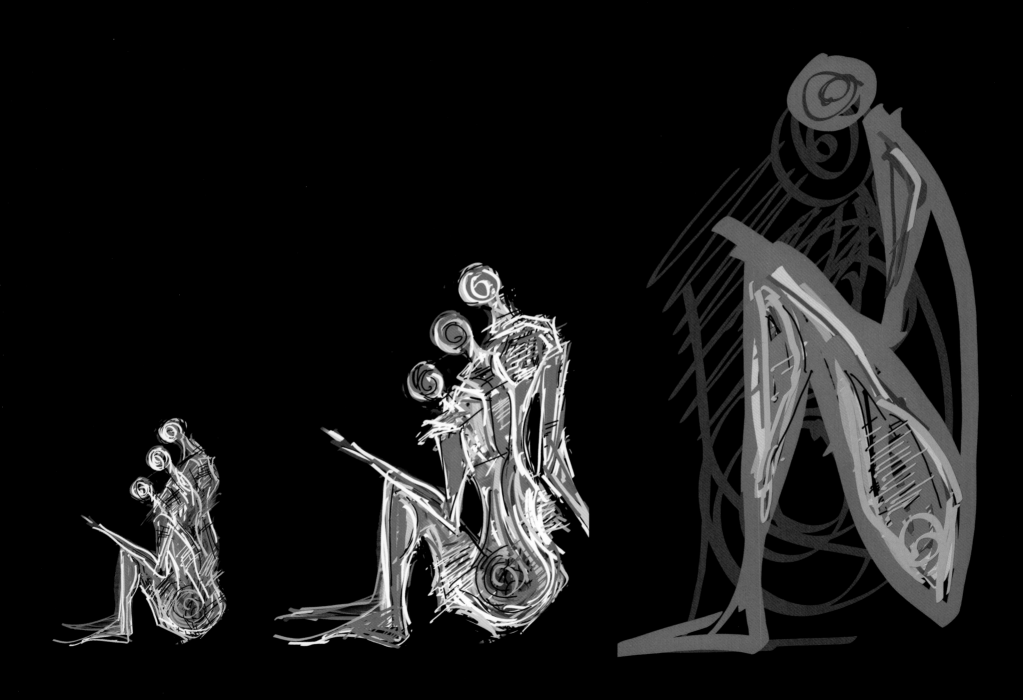

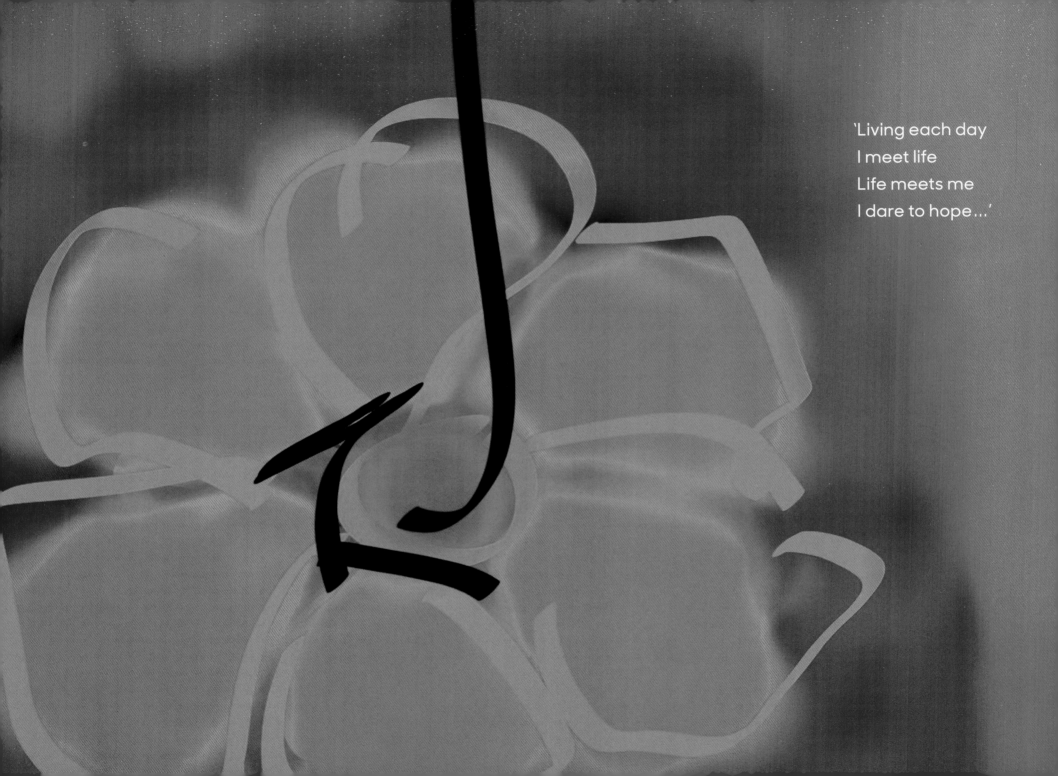

'Living each day
I meet life
Life meets me
I dare to hope...'

Why I continue to create digital art

Engaging in the act of creating art allowed me to step inside myself and really think about what being a vasculitis patient is like and what the condition has done to me. This form of self-exploration encouraged reflective thought, which helped me to see things from a different perspective and address some of the conflicts within my inner dialogue. I understood that no matter what stage you are in your life, there's always going to be change, and there's always going to be a next stage. How we respond to that change, by finding ways to adapt and work around it, is central to move into that next stage.

I found that making art supported me to harness mindfulness. When I am drawing, it's just hand-eye coordination and my mind focused on the digital canvas. When I immerse myself in creating art, no other thoughts enter my mind. Brain research shows that engaging in creative activity encourages relaxation and mindfulness. The act of creation, then, is as important as the end result.

I embarked on quite the adventure when I changed course 11 years ago. If I had not been presented with the set of challenges my illness introduced, my next stage would doubtless have been more streamlined. Nevertheless, I am richer for going through this experience, no matter how painful, frustrating and devastating it has been.

'All true artists, whether they know it or not, create from a place of no-mind, from inner stillness.'

Eckhart Tolle

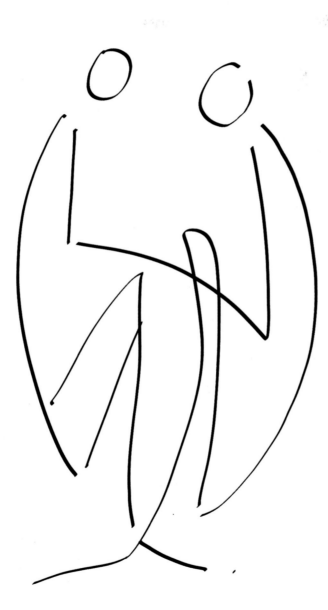

Opposite: *In Full Bloom*, 2018
Right: *Continuance*, 2019

135

How I use art to empower me

The process of drawing holds the attention of my mind. I free up my thoughts into the blank canvas, and they unfold into some colourful shape and form as my hand, eye and mind unite in cognition, abstraction and creation. Starting with a blob of colour or random lines, it gradually becomes clearer and forms a detailed picture. These drawings are not just about what I perceive with my senses, but also include the concept of my perception. For example, if I draw pain as I perceive it, I also draw the *concept* of my perception of pain. Giving pain, frustration or change a structure and form allows me to see an external representation of what is going on in my mind, expose what I am experiencing and discover what they mean to me.

Being able to describe the intensity of pain using shades of red over and over and repeatedly use concentric shapes around the hips and ankles to imply limitations and issues with mobility lets me see the bigger picture, how it all links in and my overall reaction to the concept of illness. It gives visibility and a voice to the unseen inner world and hard-to-articulate experiences. Challenging change by putting pain, fatigue, frustration and all the feelings that govern me into colour and shape helps me to get a grip and tackle those feelings better. This is empowering! It's also fun.

Creative Empowerment, 2018

'Colour is my daylong obsession, joy, and torment. What keeps my heart awake is colourful silence.'

Claude Monet

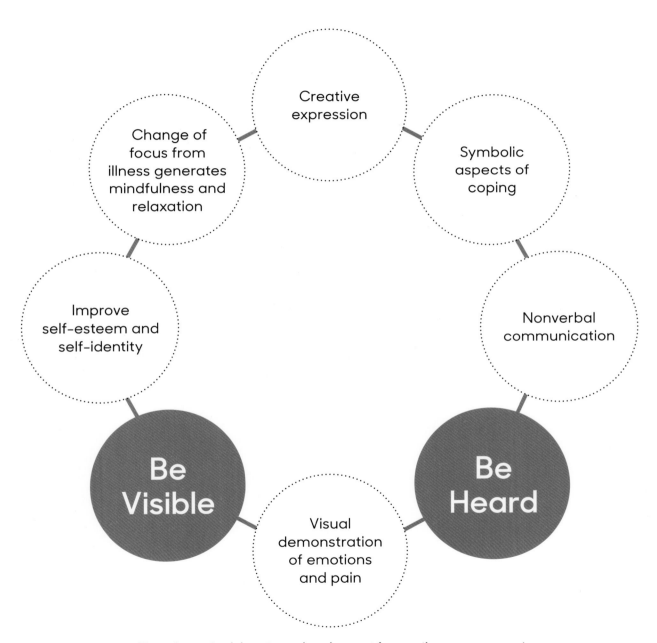

This schematic elaborates on how I use art for creative empowerment.

***Art Adds Colour and Perspective, When Skies Are Grey (Triptych)*, 2015** These are
three separate artworks I am showing here as a triptych to convey how adding
colour can be uplifting. Colour brings a vibrant energy to counter a low, muted mood.
It can change your way of looking at your illness and see beyond it, to look deeper
and see yourself from a modified perspective. It can help to make things more clear.
Sometimes it's good to cut loose and make art or look at art just for the fun of it.
After all, art isn't just about baring your soul; sometimes it's about lifting it, too.

The lotus,
keeps its head held high,
despite the rain,
storm or sunshine

The lotus, rises from the mud,
bringing beauty and strength
to the ugliness around

It is rooted to the ground,
despite how deliriously happy
or harsh,
the background becomes

Come now, be the beautiful lotus
that you are ...

Lotus, 2019

Creative Empowerment, **2017** The red illustrates the pain on the left side of
the face, across the jaw and around the left eye. The thin black lines around the
eyes signify sharp jolts of pain, as do the black and white lines across the face.
The thicker area of black in the middle of the forehead, extending down to the
middle of the face, hints at the uncertainty, apprehension and concerns that
tug at me. The blue area shows how I am trying to find calm and balance in
spite of the disarray and disruption within. The vibrant background colours are
the positive energies that surround and empower me.

Opposite: *Introspection*, **2020**

140

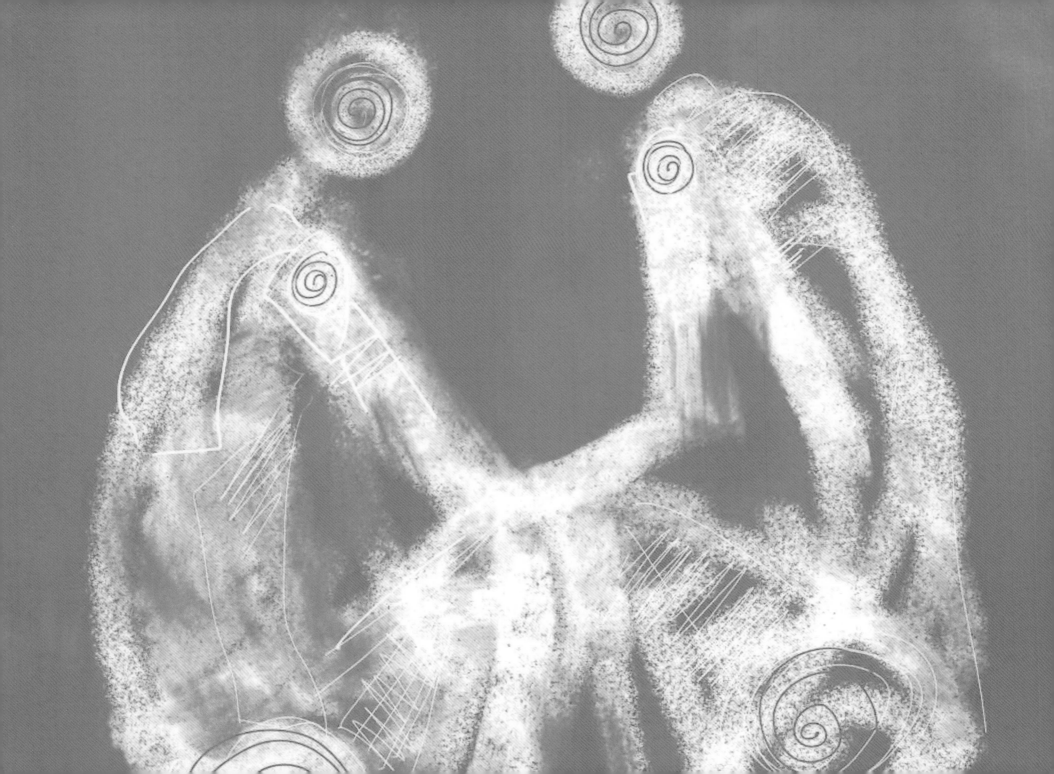

Part Four: Explore
Balancing Me

Can Art Be a Catalyst for Healing?

'Learn how to see. Realise that everything
connects to everything else.'

Leonardo da Vinci

What impact can art have on illness?

Art can play a role in transforming the narrative of illness, disability and pain. Incorporating creativity into our lifestyles can enhance interpersonal well-being and let us find balance within. Research has shown that biopsychosocial processes that facilitate creative activities can reduce anxiety, depression and stress. The entire process involved in composing visual art stimulates our imagination and incorporates multiple areas of our brain responsible for vision, memory and fine motor skills, ultimately leading to relaxation and mindfulness.

Art is an outlet, a form of healing that helps to portray the subjective experience. This can help to build endurance to cope with changes to a person's lifestyle.

Artistic expression conveys symbolic aspects of coping, highlighting underestimated and unrecognised burdens associated with everyday life. A personal narrative expressed through art provides a voice to reveal the lived experiences of illness in their complexity.

Using an app on my mobile phone to create art has had a transformative impact on my ability to manage living with illness. The potential benefits I see from facilitating self-expression through creativity, drawing from my own experiences, help me to cope and regain some control of my life, giving me a sense of purpose.

Art is a visual voice that allows for seeing beyond illness, pain, disability and life challenges. It shows the real face behind the illness, giving a bigger picture of the sociocultural influences that govern us. It highlights the stereotypes and stigmas faced by those with illnesses, especially in pluralistic societies. Art can generate newer insights and attitudinal changes to help build a culture where everyone gets visibility, a voice and inclusion.

Studies have shown that creative expression can have a favourable effect on the self-management of long-term illness by supporting well-being and providing an outlet for personal narratives.

'The pain passes, but the beauty remains.'

Pierre-Auguste Renoir

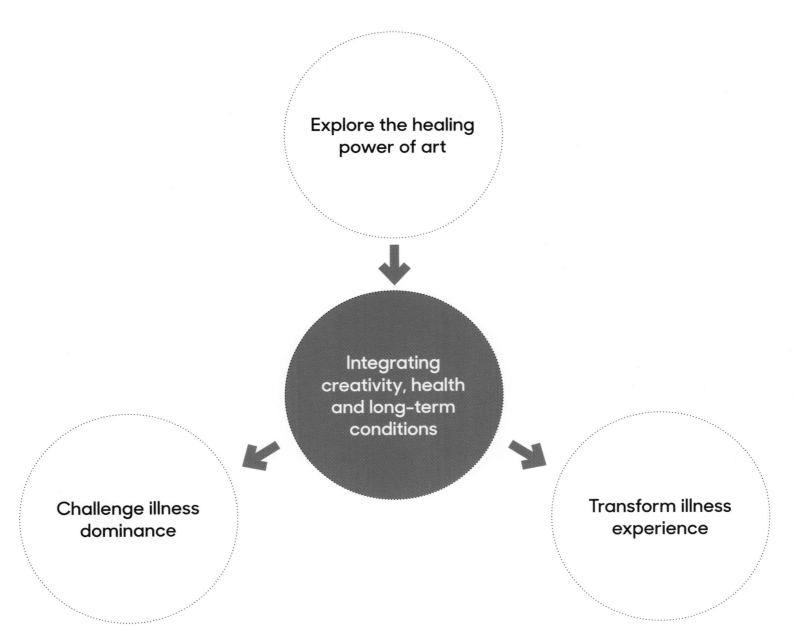

Explore the healing power of art

Integrating creativity, health and long-term conditions

Challenge illness dominance

Transform illness experience

How art can be used as a tool for positive reinforcement and reflective thinking

Art can be more than a form of expression; it is also a way of thinking. By being an outlet that portrays the subjective physical or emotional experience, it can in turn help develop self-reliance, coping strategies, social engagement and cultural inclusion.

Art was and continues to be a tool for positive reinforcement and reflective thinking for me. I managed to achieve a semblance of normality by starting to set more realistic goals and standards for me around my limitations. Medication deals with the physical dimension, but addressing the spiritual and emotional dimensions is also an integral part of the healing process. I found mindfulness through art gives me a sense of inner peace and strength to cope. Art encourages self-reflection, affects the way we see and think, the way we look at things. Reflection not only harnesses ideas; it also grows our self-awareness. It helps to deepen ourselves and our perspectives. I now need to ask the questions: How often do we reflect? At the end of the day? Occasionally? Never? Have a think about it.

When I started to reflect more and more, I found that by tapping into my inner creativity I began to see that, in spite of my physical and emotional challenges, there's still beauty within difficult situations. That brought home to me the idea of seeing the positives in the negatives and learning from them.

'Art is a line around your thoughts.'

Gustav Klimt

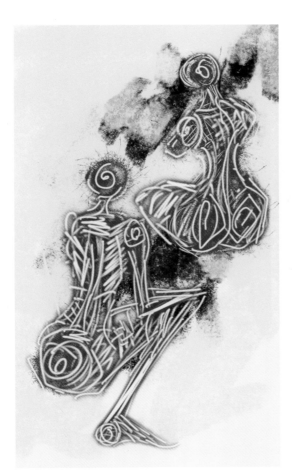

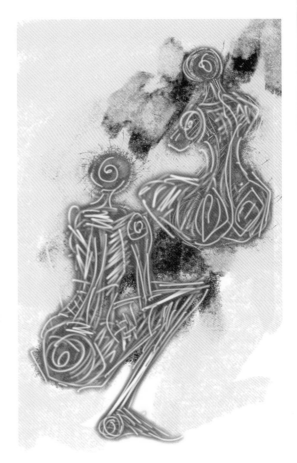

Balance, 2019
Finding a steady state within the chaos that surrounds our inner environment.

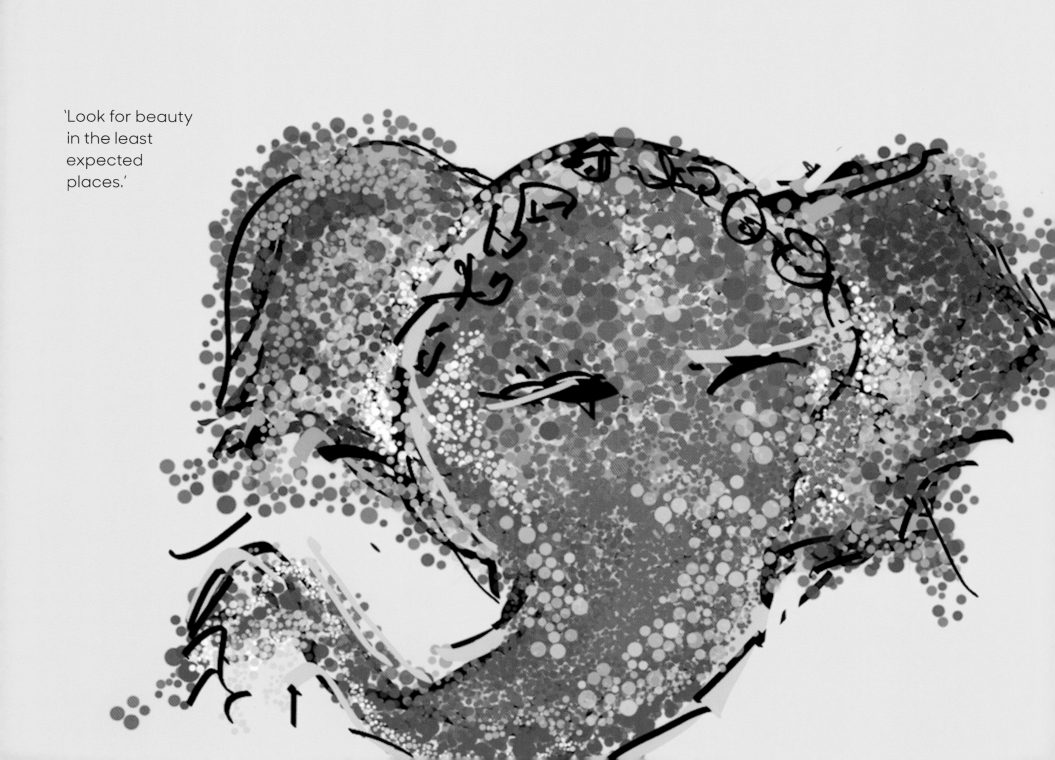

'Look for beauty in the least expected places.'

The potential therapeutic benefits of creating art

- Art can be a therapeutic intervention, given the impact of creative expression and output on self-management, supporting one's well-being

- The creative force can help people modify their lifestyles, transform challenging situations and reshape self-identity

- Art is a tool to explore further approaches to the self-management of long-term illnesses

- For many people going through illness, addressing mental or physical aspects alone is not enough

- Emotional and spiritual elements need to be considered too – art helps us do this

- Art creates a reflective space to practise mindfulness and living in the moment

- Harnessing creativity to cope with daily challenges can be a constructive as well as an enjoyable pursuit

- A wealth of studies illustrates its potential therapeutic benefits

Opposite: *Take a Bow*, **2015** Despite challenging physical and emotional circumstances, there's still beauty within unpleasant situations. And if you can't see it, create that beauty yourself.
Right: *In Full Bloom*, **2019**

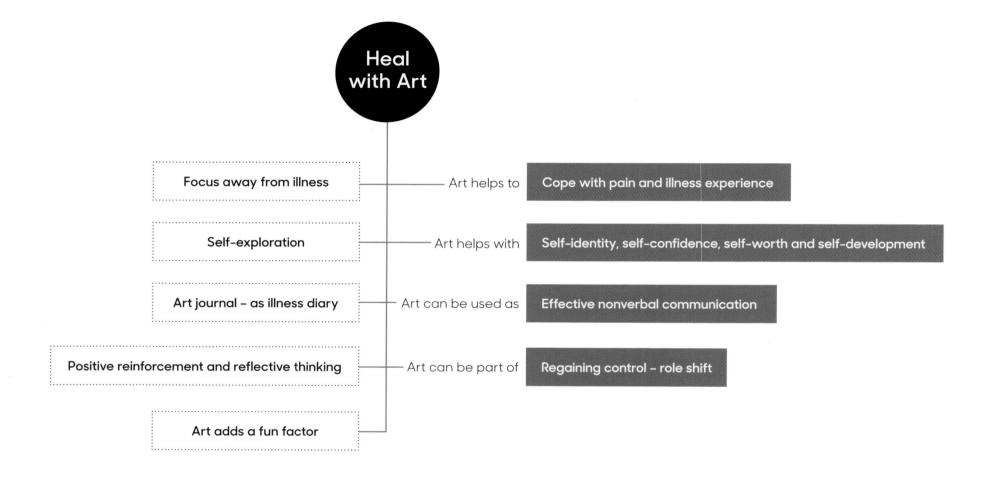

Heal with Art

Focus away from illness	Art helps to	Cope with pain and illness experience
Self-exploration	Art helps with	Self-identity, self-confidence, self-worth and self-development
Art journal – as illness diary	Art can be used as	Effective nonverbal communication
Positive reinforcement and reflective thinking	Art can be part of	Regaining control – role shift
Art adds a fun factor		

Focus away from illness This diagram outlines how art can be incorporated into the self-management of illness.

Equilibrium, 2019

What we know so far about self-exploration and creative expression

For centuries, the idea that creative expression can make a powerful contribution to the healing process has been embraced by many different cultures. The creation of circular designs has been part of spiritual practices around the world, throughout recorded history – for example, the Tibetan 'Wheel of Time', which symbolically illustrates the structure of the universe.

The Swiss psychiatrist Carl G. Jung, one of the founders of modern psychology, is credited with connecting colour to relaxation. It was his view that drawing and colouring circular shapes incorporating symmetrical, repetitive or geometric designs was a powerful calming tool.

'I sketched every morning in a notebook a small circular drawing, a mandala, which seemed to correspond to my inner situation at the time. With the help of these drawings I could observe my psychic transformations from day to day . . . My mandalas were cryptograms . . . in which I saw the self – that is, my whole being – actively at work' (*Memories, Dreams, Reflections*, C.G. Jung. Ed. Aniela Jaffe. Trans. Richard and Clara Winston. New York: Random House. 1965).

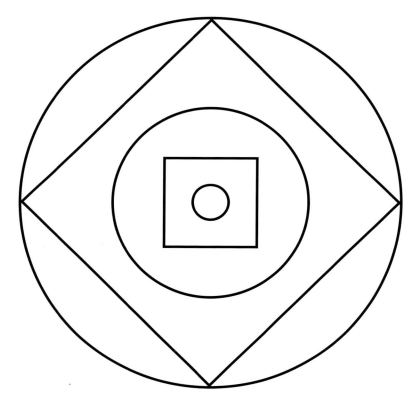

According to Carl Jung, mandalas are circular designs that reflect the wholeness of the person creating them.

Art supports my well-being by:

- Finding a meaning to what I am going through

- Positive reinforcement

- Reflection

- Having an outlet to cope and build endurance

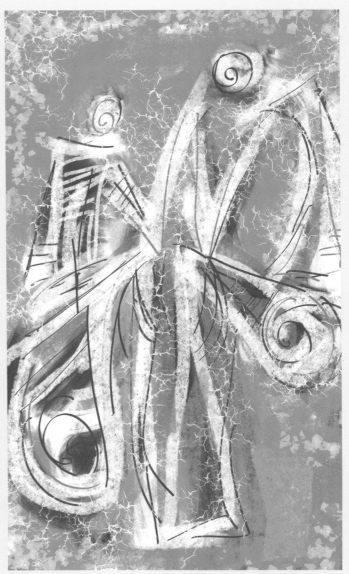

***The Art of Well-being*, 2019** We may all perceive well-being in different ways. We do not always take physical, mental and social elements into account when we think of well-being.

153

Duality, 2017

The figures on the right with differing shades of red and blue express the duality the human body goes through with illness. Protect versus destroy. On the one hand, my body supports me by protecting my organs against the illness (blue shades). On the other hand, my body is destroying my organs as part of the illness (red shades). The colour green shows a level of balance and harmony that exists between these two states. The gesture of holding hands refers to the duality of human nature. The set of images on the left show me on the right-hand corner with two others who are going through similar illness. Art reflects human emotions as well as draws on human emotions.

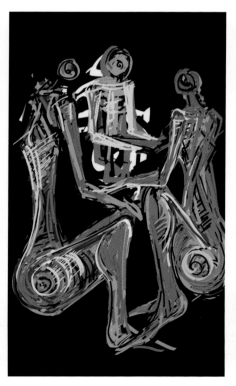
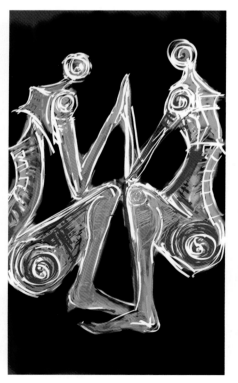

Healing with Art, 2015
Engaging in any form of creative expression through colour, shape, sound, writing or movement can be a powerful healing experience. It can be any of the following: performing arts (music, singing, theatre, dance, film); visual arts, design and craft (colouring, painting, photography, ceramics); literature (storytelling, writing, poetry, reading); electronic, online and digital arts; community, cultural festivals and fairs.

Healing with Art, 2017
Engaging in creative activities, using any form of expression
through colour, shape, sound, writing or movement can help
the healing process.

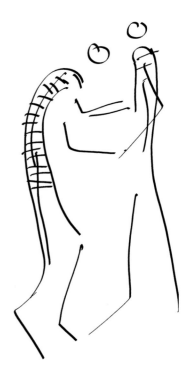

State of Being, 2019

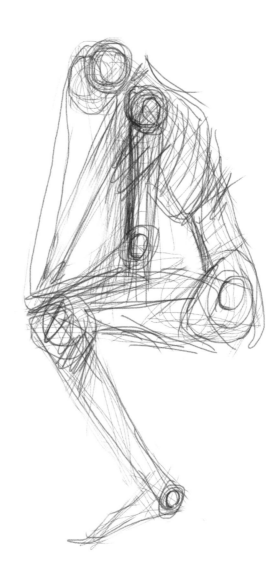

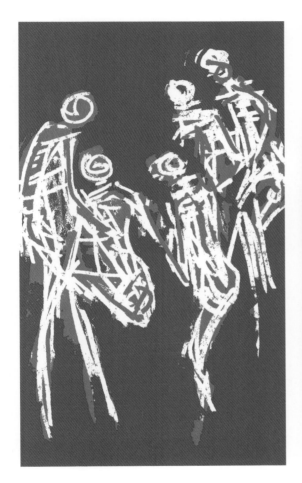

Above: *State of Being – The External Spectrum That Surrounds Us*, 2019
Opposite: *State of Being – My Invisible World*, 2019

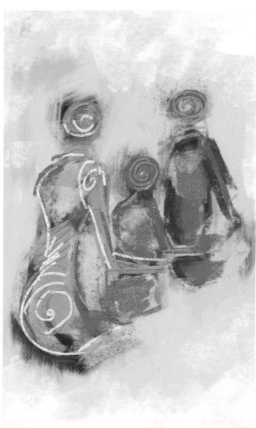

Above: *Beyond Illness*, 2019
Opposite: *Unison*, 2019

Catching your breath
as the background
changes colour
to maintain balance in
the 'act of inhaling' as
we breathe.

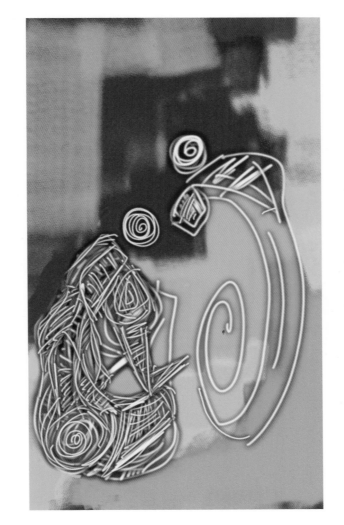

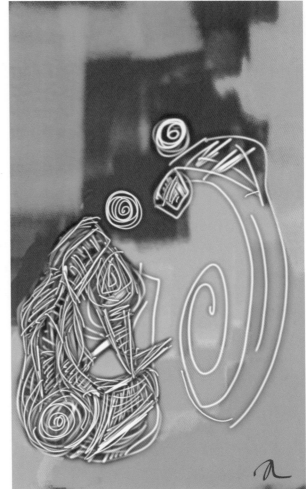

Me and My Shadow – The Inner Dialogue

Whispering I hear

As my 'consciousness' walks hand in hand with my 'shadow'

'Is it my shadow? Or is it yours?' consciousness asks shadow

'I stand with you,' says consciousness. 'Do you stand with me, shadow?'

'Look who's talking,' says shadow, 'you or me?'

'You keep saying, I only cast your gloom

And, now you ask whether I stand with you?'

Arguing with shadow

Laughing with shadow

Running away from shadow

Catching up with shadow

Engaging with shadow

Embracing shadow

Trying to feel superior to shadow

Feeling inferior to shadow

Avoiding shadow

Seeking shadow

Stepping out with shadow

In tune with shadow

Touching shadow

Shrugging off shadow

Supporting shadow

Rejecting shadow

Liberating from shadow

Returning to shadow

Being kind to shadow

Being angry at shadow

Forgiving shadow

Reflecting with shadow

Respecting shadow

Empowering shadow

A step closer to being synchronous with shadow?

A step closer to inner-life 'consciousness'

and outer-life 'shadow'

To be in vibrational harmony?

Resonating as one?

Whispering stops

All is still

Well, well

Is this indeed a step closer to being in sync with my 'whole' self?

Opposite and right: *Me and My Shadow*, 2020

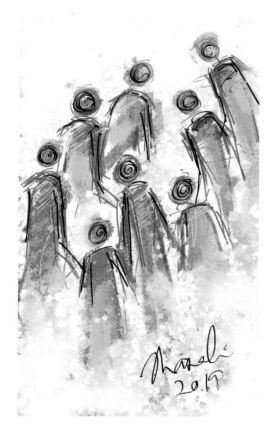  

Beyond Illness, 2020, 2018 and 2018

Part Five: Engage
Connect with Me

'Art is not what you see but what
you make others see.'

Edgar Degas

Bringing others into the picture

For centuries, across civilisations, creative expression has been used as part of healing rituals. Creative expression has undeniable sustainable power, providing valuable insights into what it's like to be human. There is something about creativity, how we engage with it and share it with others that impacts our health.

Using art as a platform **engages the community**, giving it a wider perspective on the true reality and mystery of the human experience with illness; conveying the symbolic aspects of coping demonstrates emotion. This engages the viewer to recognise both the emotion in the artwork and their own emotions while observing the artwork. Becoming mindful of one's own emotional response opens up a greater capacity for empathy – that is, one person understanding another person's situation and what they are feeling. This is definitely one of the keys to changing one's attitudes towards illness.

Engaging with others gives rise to more visibility, providing a voice for the unrecognised burdens associated with living with illness every day. My work is centred on generating awareness about **creative engagement** to combat the challenges of illness experience, generating interest in how expressions of the 'lived experience' can help health practitioners and the public gain new insights.

'If you want to convey fact, this can only ever be done through a form of distortion. You must distort to transform what is called appearance into image.'

Francis Bacon

Opposite: *In Full Bloom*, 2020

I want to start more conversations about using art in dialogue

Being both a doctor and a patient, I gained a unique perspective on the journey of art and the human experience. Articulating the lived experience, especially with complex long-term conditions, can be difficult. As I had no formal art training, my work comes from within. Emotions, pain, fatigue, and humour, too, are my cues for expressing the changes surrounding me.

Living with a long-term condition is like being on a roller-coaster ride, with regular ups and downs. There will be good spells and bad spells. Symptoms may vary, and the days may vary. And beyond the symptom, there are other influences as well: emotional, cultural, social or political. In short, it makes things complex. Old routines are abandoned, and previously simple tasks become difficult. The mind and the body have to adapt.

In exploring art and the human factor, my digital canvases highlight hidden realities of what the 'lived experience' looks like with long-term illness. Through my art, I want to share the presentation and representation of rare chronic illnesses and how the creative force has empowered me and how it helped me to regain control, manage and move forward from overpowering emotions and the challenges my condition caused in me. My art represents social inclusion and respect for all people subjected to stereotyping and stigma due to illness or disability.

'Art is not a handicraft. It is the transmission of feeling the artist has experienced.'

Leo Tolstoy

Opposite: *In Full Bloom*, 2019

Communicating the wider perspective with art

Art can create a common language to highlight and address poorly addressed issues that revolve around people living with chronic ill health. It invites a collective understanding of how people make sense of key life experiences and what it means to them. Art can help you see the complexities and the fluid state of the lived experience with long-term illness.

Sharing my experience of art with others can certainly help people think about newer ways to cope with what they are going through as well as look at the illness – theirs and mine – in a different light.

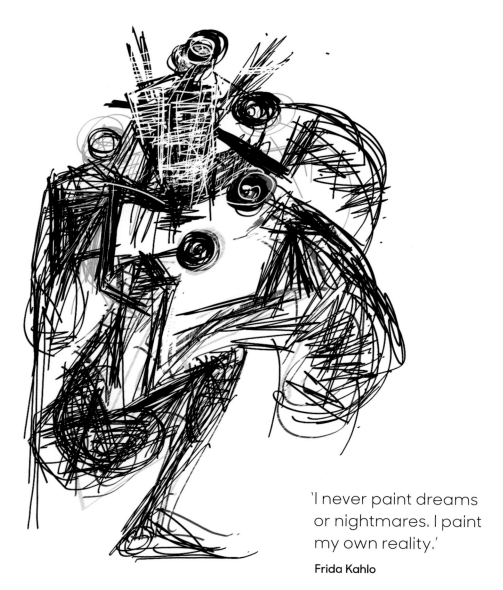

'I never paint dreams or nightmares. I paint my own reality.'
Frida Kahlo

Solidarity, 2019

I would like to see more art in dialogue, communicating and disseminating how art can help friends, family, the public and health providers see the multiplicity, the fluid state, the 'calm, the storm and the in-between' of the lived experience.

This can help to:

- Open dialogue, raise awareness and create agency about facilitating expressions of illness

- Show how visual expressions can be an alternate language, communicating the clinical process and complexities of the lived experience to a wider audience

- Highlight the potential impact of facilitating expressions of illness experience and generate interest among others to engage in creative activities

- Empower people to feel in control of their own health and use creative ways to improve their health

Balance, 2019

Balance, **2019**
How does it feel to live with an illness on a daily basis?

How do people make sense of it?

The multifactorial nature of illness.

Living with an uncertain future

Communication   Change   Attitudes   Complexity   Challenges

Connecting with health teams is a way of highlighting the idea of changing perceptions about health, using creative expressions as a voice for the lived experiences of illness in their complexity. Drawing attention to how expressions of the illness experience can open ways of knowing and learning to help health practitioners find a deeper understanding of what people go through and the impact illness has on image, identity and self-worth.

A great deal of diagnostic power can be drawn from the visual world, opening tangential ways of learning, helping to explore our understanding of the human aspect of medical practice. Representation of illness expressed through art can help to bridge the gap between the biomedical and the human focus, as well as break down some of the complexities of communication encountered in multidisciplinary health environments. In the patient-clinician conversation, expressing illness through art can help healthcare providers to:

- Step out of the comfort zone, opening channels for communication, making room for difficult conversations and creating a common language to deal with poorly addressed issues

- See the patient as a person first

- See more of the person behind the illness

Whether as healthcare professionals, educators or the general public, we can all use art to promote adaptive coping and the self-management of illnesses. Art can also foster inner reflection and facilitate detailed clinical observations and outside-the-box thinking around clinical practice and the everyday experience of healthcare. There is much work and research being done worldwide looking at art as a tool in health promotion, prevention and illness management.

'Art is the queen of all sciences communicating knowledge to all the generations of the world.'

Leonardo da Vinci

Visual arts can help us explore our understanding of the human aspect of illness:

What does **pain** look like?

What does **living with illness** look like?

What does **change** look like?

What does **losing control** look like?

What does a **good support system** look like?

Overlap, 2019

'Art is the expression of the profoundest thoughts in the simplest way.'

Albert Einstein

When I create images, in many cases I am painting portraits of illness, my illness, and colour is one of the main ways I'm able to represent the thoughts and feelings that illness engenders. The illness tries to assert authority over me, my work and lifestyle.

Art helps me to separate the various strands and reason out the conflicts I am going through with my inner self. It unravels the multifactorial nature of illness – the patterns of pain, fatigue, isolation and vulnerability, the variability in my day and the shifting dynamics as embodied expressions. I capture a broad spectrum of issues – what 'anticipation' of new symptoms or worsening of symptoms feels like, the 'uncertainty', the changes and challenges that accompany the illness trajectory and my emerging 'resilience' to regain control as both a mind and bodily experience. I have been exploring objectifying the subjective and my take on human resilience, reflecting and illustrating the inner-body experience of restoring balance amidst a state of constant transitions.

Art was a mode to break down barriers within myself and open up conversations, a way to tap into my human resilience and challenge the complexity and change brought on by my illness. It helped me to dig into the 'who, what and where' I am at this point in my life. Art was my way of finding me beyond illness.

Colour is such a personal subject. Often, we don't even realise this until we share our work with others. I use colours at the red end of the spectrum to show pain as well as joy and connection, as those colours have a stimulatory effect on me: positive and negative.

A colour that may mean 'happy' to me may mean 'sad' to someone else. It's only through continuing to create work that you'll come to realise how important colour is and what it means to you. You may not even be aware of it at first, but you'll soon see that patterns and habits will start to emerge: 'Why do I always use this colour when I want to show pain; why does this colour make me feel happy?' This is how we can use art to discover more about ourselves, to find out who we are and explore the grey areas within us.

Portraits of Illness, **2019**

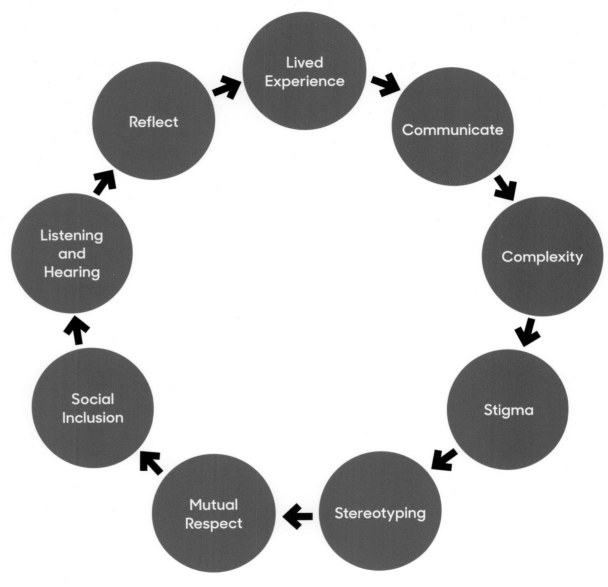

Right: Virtuous circle of interconnections
This shows the various factors that influence and play an integral part in forming interrelationships with others around me. The elements that encircle me, beyond the physical illness. They are the shared challenges between home-, work- and social-health settings and me.

Opposite: *Everyday Transitions*, **2017**
Giving visibility and voice, the bigger picture, the human factor in the public eye.

Opposite: *Interconnections*, **2016**
I use my art to represent social inclusion and respect for people subjected to stereotyping and stigma due to illness or disability. It highlights the lived experience and the sociocultural-political struggles and challenges faced. Social stigma, stereotyping, attitudes, fears, influences from cultural and spiritual beliefs can make the illness experience an emotionally draining encounter. Changing social attitudes towards illness and disability is key to moving forward.

Right: *My Inner Rhythm*, **2019**
Regaining a sense of control, a sense of purpose, inspired forwards movement with my lifestyle.

Transitions and shifting dynamics

The colour and movement in this image reveals the interplay between the following elements:

- Chaos and calm – the red and blue figures
- Engaging with change – the orange figure
- Connecting to break isolation – the pink figure

It shows the inner rhythm that communicates the complex interactions and the fluidity of the lived experience arising from the impact of illness.

My Inner Rhythm, 2019

My day-to-day brain

This is a representation of what goes on in my brain day to day. The figures depict communication both at a micro and macro level within the brain to maintain **balance**, **harmony** and a **steady state** in the midst of ongoing chaos.

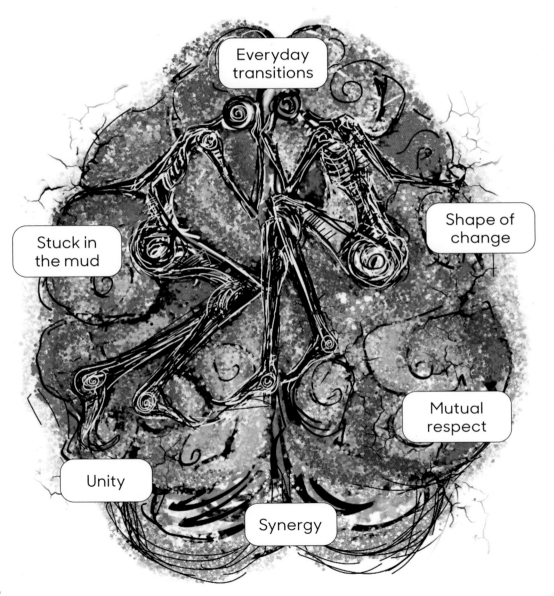

My Brain, 2019

183

The Days of Calm, Storm and the In-between, 2019

'The days of "the in-between"

The days between "the calm" and "the storm"

The days that are neither here nor there

The days I struggle to keep up with

These are the days

You see me …

Do you see my pain?'

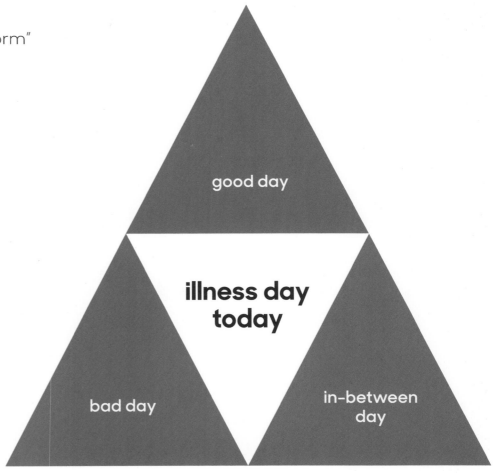

The realities of my lived experience
Each day flows differently. Sometimes
the variation is minimal; that is a good day.
When it is dominated by pain or fatigue, it
is a bad day. The rest are in-between days.

Above: *Calm, Storm and the In-between,* 2019
Putting a face to change, a shape to shifting roles and transitions, I
explore the power of expressing and symbolising frustrations and feelings
about the illness by taking the focus away and building endurance.
Opposite: *The Calm, the Storm and the In-between,* 2017

The In-Between

Where do I begin?

The day I stopped being the person I knew and became someone new

The day I lost my dreams and expectations?
When it seemed I was given an opportunity to grow amidst misfortune
When it seemed I was given a chance to find clarity amidst inner chaos

The days I feel betrayed, abandoned and disempowered?
When I feel so tired I can't seem to think
When I feel so listless I can't seem to move
When I feel so fatigued I strain to speak
When I feel so powerless I feel loss of control

The days I feel the simmering of conflicts within?
When the noise of emotional turmoil gets louder
When living feels harder than just existing
When I feel lost and stranded and unable to see beyond
These are 'the in-between' days
The days between 'the calm' and 'the storm'
The days when the pain is at a varying rhythm
The days,
I smile
I laugh
I carry on

Oh, but the pain can be deafening
It is sometimes physical
It is sometimes emotional
It is sometimes both
The pain is not always visible!

These are the days
You see me
You don't see my pain
The days of 'the in-between'

The days between 'the calm' and 'the storm'
The days I carry on despite inner battles
The days I struggle to keep up with
The days that are neither here nor there

Now, you see me
Now, do you see my pain?

I am "living" each day
I feel triumphant as I face them all
The calm, the storm and the in-between days
Am not alone
You see me through it all

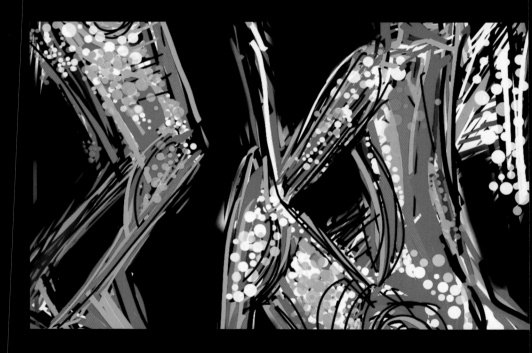

Making the Invisible Visible, 2018
My work gives visibility and a voice to often
hidden emotional, spiritual and cultural
impacts and comments on the sociopolitical
influences that govern us.

'Living each day
I meet life
Life meets me
I dare to hope'

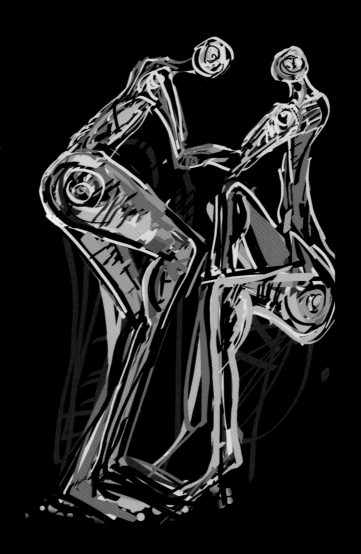

'The power of social
engagement,
cultural inclusion
and mutual respect.'

Opposite: *Art in Dialogue,* 2018
Right: *Seeing Beyond the Illness,* 2017
People facing illness, disability and other
health challenges have the *freedom to
express* themselves without physical,
social or attitudinal barriers.

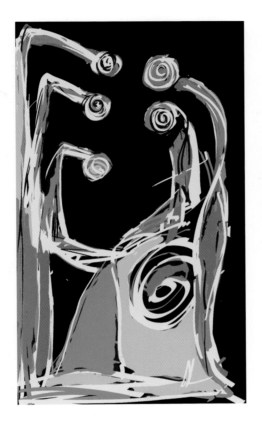

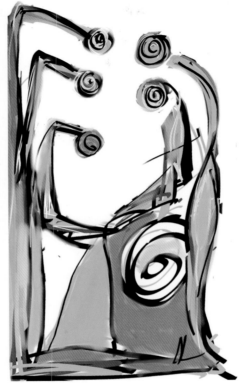

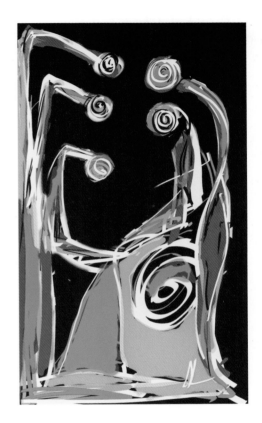

Opposite: *Rapport,* 2016, 2017
By engaging in the arts, people with
illnesses and disabilities can connect
and contribute to their communities.

Above: *Connecting with Others,* 2017
To be seen, heard and included
gives more control over day-to-day
activities.

Connecting with Others, 2018

Finding Connections within Connections, 2016
Harnessing your creative potential despite
your limitations and however difficult
circumstances may be and sharing
these experiences with others cultivates
a connection within your own self and
with others.

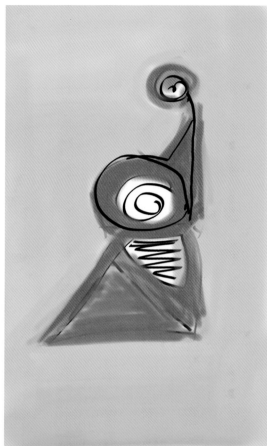

Above: *Power of Inclusion*, 2018, 2017 and 2018
Collaboration builds interpersonal relationships.

Opposite: *Inclusion*, 2018
To be seen, heard and included breaks the isolation.

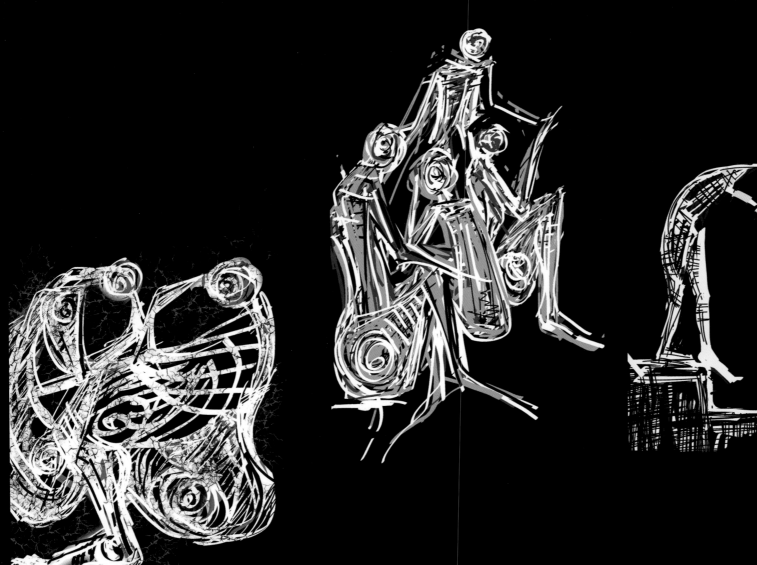
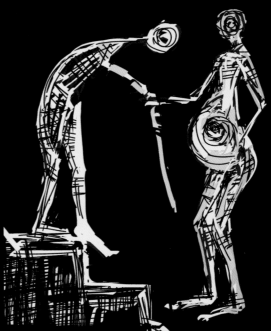

Opposite: *Social Engagement and Cultural Inclusion,* **2016**
Accepting and including in everyday life a classmate, friend, family member or work colleague with a disability, pain, or a long-term or terminal illness is a start.
Right: *Mutual Respect,* **2018**

199

Mutual Respect, 2019

These images represent social inclusion and respect for people subjected to stereotyping and stigma due to illness or disability. They aim to direct people's attention to the mental and physical anguish and strain that engulf the lived experience of illness. They speak about the power of mutual respect, social engagement and cultural inclusion to uplift and alleviate the situation for a person living through illness.

'The days I carry on
despite inner battles

The days I struggle
to keep up with

You see me
Do you see my pain?'

Visibility, 2019

Above and opposite: *Support, 2019*

202

Above and opposite: *Support*, 2019

'I am "living" each day
I feel triumphant as I face
them all
The calm, the storm
and the in-between days
I am not alone
You see me through it all'

Fellowship

'I stumble
I fall
I break
I mend
I get back up

The days I struggle
to keep up
You see me
Do you see my pain?'

Fellowship, **2018**
The bigger picture, 'the human factor' in the public eye.

Part Six: Evoke
Art, Change and Me

'The secret of change is to focus all of your energy
not on fighting the old, but on building the new.'

Socrates

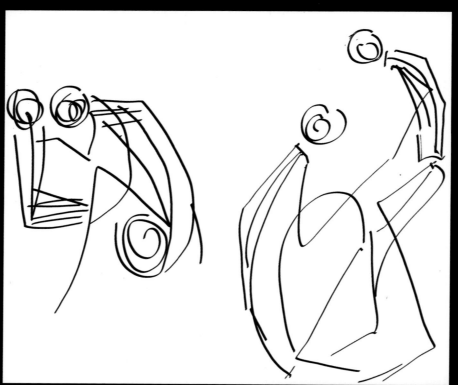

Collective influence and social engagement through art

Does art influence you? Art can be a way to:

- understand emotions and empathise

- communicate ideas visually

- examine sociopolitical, religious and cultural issues that influence personal beliefs

Art is more than a form of expression. It is a way of thinking, an outlet that portrays the subjective illness experience.
  Can you go beyond being inspired by art and evoke personal and social change?

- Art has the capacity to engage the community and aid social transformation

- By engaging in the arts, people with illnesses and disabilities can connect and contribute to their communities

- Sharing through creative expression with others breaks the isolation and can also help others understand emotions and empathise with pain, illness or disabilities

- Connecting and communicating what the lived experience is like with others certainly can help them to change attitudes and perceptions

- Art can challenge existing stereotypes and stigma around illness and disability

- Sharing experiences of using the digital medium for creativity enables people with limited hand function to participate in art, too

- Using art as a platform to engage the community and generate change can help build a truly representative culture

- This certainly will be a step towards evoking personal and social change

'The principles of true art is not to portray, but to evoke.'

Jerzy Kosinski

Opposite: *Proximity*, **2018**
How art can inspire, influence and enable change.

211

What am I trying to say with my art? I am trying to evoke change

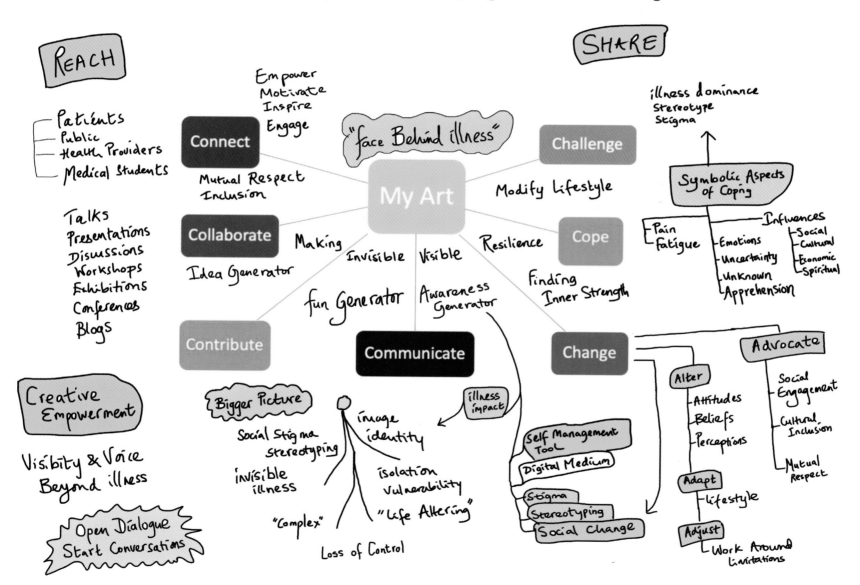

How can art help people with long-term illness and disabilities?

The nature of a chronic illness is such that it is a process, an unending roller-coaster ride that can take in new symptoms, side effects from drugs, flare-ups and mood swings.

Maintaining a balancing act between coping, adapting and controlling the pain and one's emotional state is part of this process.

Facing repetitive challenges takes courage, determination and perseverance. Social stigma, stereotyping, attitudes, fears, influences from various cultural and spiritual beliefs can make this experience mentally exhausting.

The arts have the potential to assist in promoting health and healing. Visual art is a powerful tool for me, to manage my illness along with medications and other therapies. The use of art in healing combines the emotional, physical, creative, spiritual and social dimensions and deals not only with the illness and symptoms but also with me as a whole person. It is truly a holistic activity. None of us, after all, is just one thing; we are all made of multiple elements.

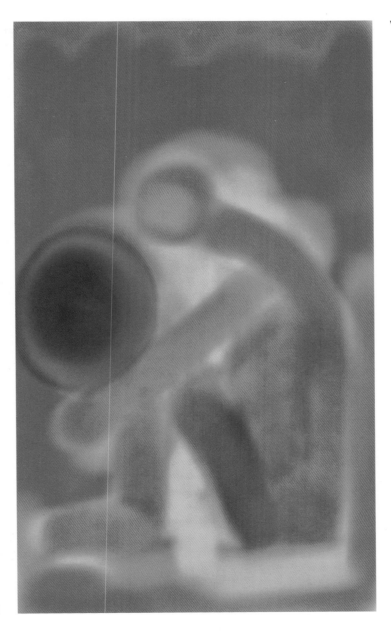

'There are two distinct languages. There is the verbal, which separates people… and there is the visual that is understood by everybody.'

Yaacov Agam

Carrying the World on My Arms, 2015

213

How art can change attitudes and challenge
existing stereotypes and stigma around illness:

- Art has no barriers, no boundaries and no conditions

- Art is limitless, offering infinite possibilities of gathering
  information from looking, engaging and appreciating
  what we see

- Art encourages self-reflection, looking inwards, the way
  we see and think

- We can use art to liberate thoughts, generate and
  champion ideas using colour, shape and movement as a
  source of information

- Using art to put the spotlight on existing stereotypes and
  stigma around illness and disability can be a prompt for
  people to pause and deliberate

- This way, art can confront stereotypes and stigma
  around illness and disability

- Art can be the spark that ignites and evokes change
  in our attitudes and behaviours over stereotyping and
  stigmatising

'Above all, see me as a person
first, my fellow co-human.'

Curious Case of Humanistic Skills, 2019

'I stumble

I fall

I break

I mend

I get back up

I walk past life's stolen moments

Shadows that haunt of shattered dreams

Glimpsing reflections of who I was

I feel triumphant as I face them all

The calm, the storm and the

in–between days.'

Changing our personal attitudes towards illness and disability is key to moving forward.

Interconnections, 2018

Curious Case of Humanistic Skills, 2019

Together We Are Power, **2019**
'Transcending illness using art defies the illness defining you.' After losing myself to the illness, my first step towards reinventing my identity was using the creative process. The social inclusion and engagement brought on by creativity was a powerful healing experience.

'Be a rainbow in someone else's cloud.'

Maya Angelou

218

Creative expression through art can be a tool to transform pain, illness and disability.

Together We Are Power, 2017–2019

Above: *Reshaping Rhythm,* **2019** Adaptive coping with newer ways to work around limitations and integrating creativity to healing can reshape the illness experience.

Opposite: *Collective Strength,* **2017**
The collective force supported and steered me forwards.

Opposite and above: *Collective Strength,* 2017

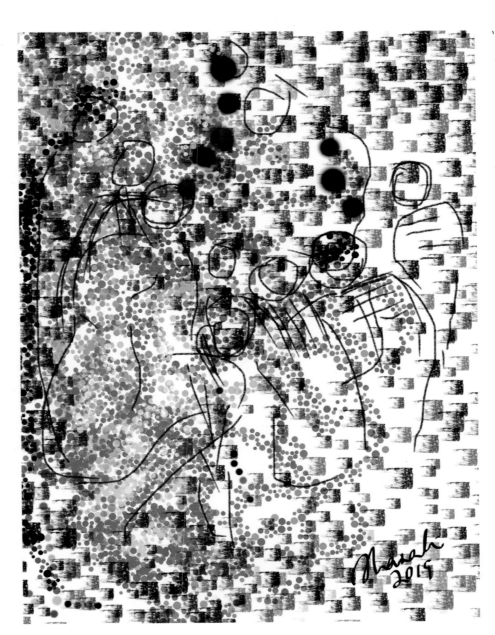

'Love and compassion are necessities, not luxuries. Without them, humanity cannot survive.'

The Dalai Lama

Opposite: *The Power of a Helping Hand,* 2016–2017
Right: *Curious Case of Humanistic Skills,* 2019
Could we all have moments to stop and think?
Is humanity slowly dying in society?
Take a moment to pause and reflect.

225

Reviving the Threads of Humanity, 2019
The social engagement, cultural inclusion and mutual respect brought on through creativity is power. It helps build a community and culture that embraces everyone.

'The greatness of humanity is not in being human, but in being humane.'

Mahatma Gandhi

The power of togetherness is about:

- Social engagement, cultural inclusion at a community level and mutual respect

- Raising public awareness on the 'lived experience' and seeing beyond illness

- Collective strength

- Challenging existing stereotypes and stigma around illness and disability

A society truly representative of everyone.

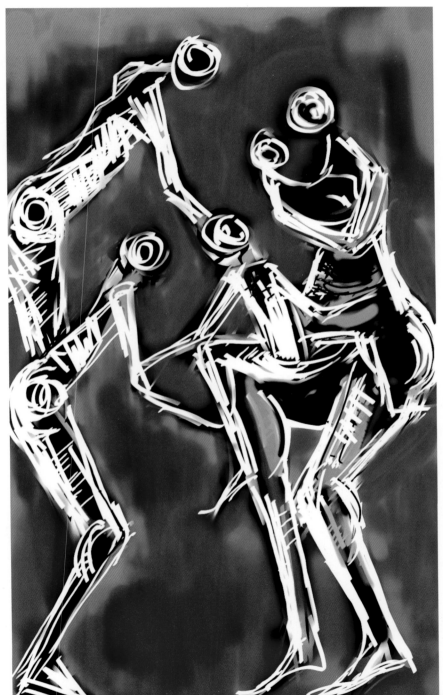

Togetherness, 2017

Right and opposite:
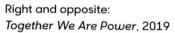
Together We Are Power, 2019
The colour filters here show the interchanging demeanours in attitudes and perceptions when it comes to seeing the person beyond illness and connecting with them. Orange is about warmth in connecting. Yellow is the stability connecting brings, and teal is clarity and understanding about the need for connecting.

'Strength of compassion
Power of togetherness
Is my voice of hope

Living each day
I meet life
Life meets me

I dare to hope
Do you?'

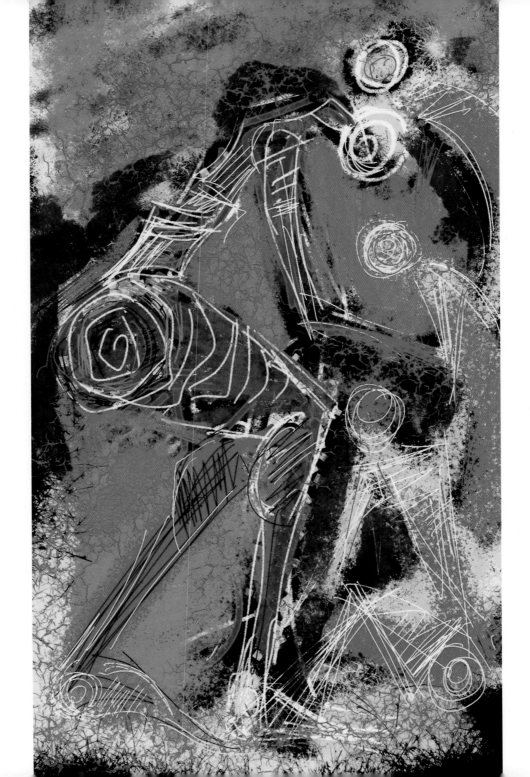

Unconditional

'You gave me hope
when there was none

You believed in me at times
when I did not

You are always with me'

Right and opposite:
Unconditional, 2017

Above and opposite: *Unconditional*, 2017

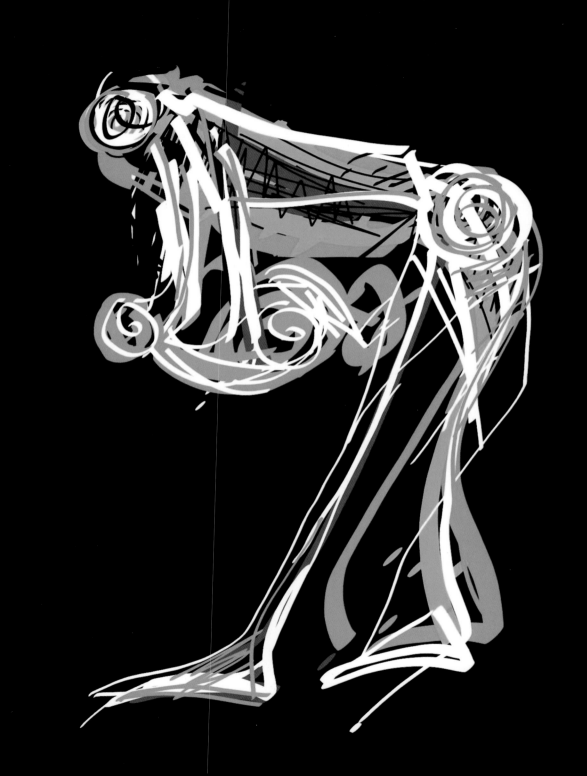

Opposite: *Unity*, **2019**
My concept 'creative empowerment
– exploring the healing power of art'
is about bringing the community
on board, to see beyond illness
and disability.

Right: *Unity*, **2018, 2019**
Using art to give visibility and a voice
to often hidden emotional, spiritual,
cultural and social impacts resulting
from living with illness helps others gain
a wider perspective on the subject.

What was

What is

What becomes

Left and opposite:
Shape of Change,
2019

It's easy to get wrapped up in an overwhelming fear of the unknown, and taking the first steps on a new road is always the hardest part – especially when you do not know where that road leads. But it's the very act of taking those first steps that is the biggest breakthrough. It means you've accepted that you need to move towards change. The 'shape' of that change will become clear as your journey continues.

In the repeated image above, let your eye move from left to right, seeing how blue tones gradually develop, and in the figure on the right, there is a dash of white. This colour progression for me indicates a sense of calm and stability in accepting change. For you, representing change may take a completely different form. The important thing is that before you can depict change, you need to recognise and accept your need for it.

'I exist
I survive
I endure
I withstand
I meet life

Living each day
Life meets me
I dare to hope'

Pillars of Strength, 2017
Facing repetitive challenges
takes courage, determination,
perseverance and a good
support network.

***Pillars of Strength*, 2019** The different filters used here show the stark contrast between black-and-white imagery and the more subtle contrasts that appear when the background colour changes, as in the middle image, and when the images and the background both change colour (the far right image). The degrees of support others can offer can be of similar contrasts, openly visible as the black-and-white image, or more silent and not so visible as the other two variants.

Right, below and opposite: *Solidarity*, 2019

These image variants depict the strength of unity between people sharing the same ideals as they stand together to make a difference and challenge existing attitudes, prejudices, stereotypes and the stigma around illness and disability. The changes in the background filter show the potential variations of this strength. The figures in the middle hold the circle of hope, the power of mutual respect, inclusion and unity. The first two images, starting from the left, show red swirls around the bodies to symbolise the power of solidarity. The swirl of blue shows the need for connecting with ourselves and others. Green spirals and lines show balance and harmony, brought on by these connections. Above all, see me as a person first, a fellow co-human.

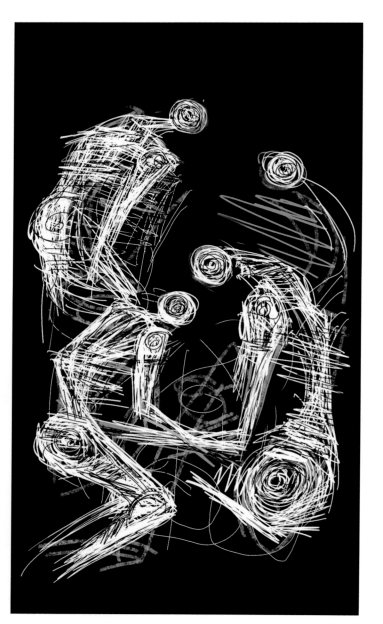

'I am "living" each day
I feel triumphant
as I face them all
The calm, the storm
and the in-between days

I am not alone
You see me through it all'

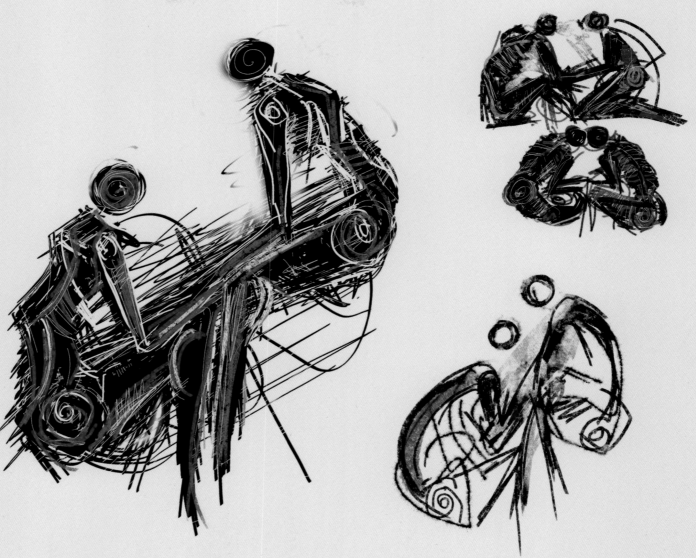

Solidarity, 2019

The strength of

The growth of

The start of

The Struggle - Taming the Beasts Within

The noise grows louder
Almost deafening me
Will it ever stop? No, it's only getting bolder
So must I

The stinging, burning, gnawing pains and the endless fatigue
become but a shadow as the rapids start forming,
aiding yet another storm about to break

Surely, it'll pass like the ones before
But what of the lingering noise?
From the ripple effects tearing through
the innermost layers and the workings of my body
I must withstand the ravages of long-term illness

I want to run, my legs won't move
I want to scream and shout, my lips hardly move
I see my reflection, a distorted image I struggle to recognise
Yes, the noise is loud and bold indeed!

What of it?
Rapids form, the tide dies down and the storm passes
The cycle continues with tidal waves that come and go
The dynamics perpetually changing and shifting shape
So, must I

The noise remains
What of it?
Let it be
Let it be a mere hum among the buzz of everyday life

Layers Within, 2017

The high tide will rise and fall
So will the battles with endurance and pain
A recurring theme
Yet,
The unforeseen chaos that suddenly entered my life has given rise
to an unexpected inner freedom
The darkest moments have seen the emerging face of resilience

I grow stronger than before
I face not these rapids, tides and my treacherous self, alone
The collective force,
supporting and steering me forwards is ever present
Together we stand
Together we are power!

Self-inquiry using art:

- Art is universal, accessible to all

- Art makes room for reflection, looking inwards, the way we see and think

- This cultivates a deeper connection with oneself, expanding on our understanding of who we are, exposing our depths and our inner truths

- Art assists **self-development** this way by enriching **self-exploration** and **self-reflection**

- Art can increase our understanding of the human condition by nurturing self-awareness

- Art can increase our awareness of empathy

- Art breaks down barriers, opens dialogue and raises awareness, helping others see the unseen and vary their perception

Art is richly complex; the possibilities of learning from it are endless…

Introspection, 2019

Challenge struggles with stigma, stereotyping and labelling

Given the chance, art can influence, inspire and evoke change at an individual and collective level.

'Let's use art to champion change.
Let us be that change!'

'Be the change that you
wish to see in the world.'

Mahatma Gandhi

Shape of change, 2017

'Let us make our
future now, and let
us make our dreams
tomorrow's reality.'

Malala Yousafzai

Above and opposite: *Bee the Change,* 2015–2020

Bee the change:

Learning new ways to take charge,
Exploring new tools.

Finding outlets:

to take the focus away,
to cope with stress,
to build endurance,
to instil calmness,
to discover inner strengths,
can help deal with situations better.

'Art can be more than a form of expression;
it can also be a way of thinking.'

Up the Tempo, 2018

Part Seven: Early Encounters
Playful Me

A play with pixels – remembering to have fun

I was playing with the doodle function on the Viber app on my mobile phone. That's how it all began.

Soon, I was playing with the doodle function's lips, stars, hats and bows. I had forgotten to laugh during those early days of my condition, and this was a reminder to find space in my life for fun when it would have been easy to only think about pain and change and illness. My outlet became butterflies and cats with bowties, elephants, owls, spiders and parrots with top hats. They certainly made me smile.

Some of my 'fun' doodles are from my early experiments in digital art, and they show how my painting style has changed and progressed as my technical ability and my understanding of who I am have developed.

The images on the pages that follow represent the playful side of my nature, my take on the lighter side of the cycle of life.

The collections *Missy Lipilicious*, *Take a Bow*, *Up the Tempo*, *Sunny Side Up* and *Trumpet Calls* are meant to be amusing, lively and spirited. I think the images also show that I've lived on three continents. The elephants, spiders and butterflies show my connection to Sri Lanka, where I grew up, while the exotic birds represent my time in the West Indies. As for the bees, they are the symbol of my new hometown of Manchester – and the owls are typically British, too. And the cats? Well, I just like cats!

'Creativity is intelligence having fun.'

Albert Einstein

Missy Lipilicious (2015)

In this collection, I playfully experiment with hairstyles and face shapes using lips and moustaches, flowers and stars from the Viber doodle tools. I show noses as moustaches because my own nostrils remind me of a moustache. I was struggling with my image when I created these images. The shape of my face and the texture of my hair had changed. So had my body shape. Minute residual effects from my facial palsy mean that the left side of my face droops, my speech can sometimes slur, and there's slight drooling at times, especially after prolonged periods of talking. All this contributed to how I saw myself in the mirror, and it left me in need of uplifting. From that aspect, these images are expressions of femininity and imperfection, of accepting change and being confident of your appearance *now*, irrespective of what you thought of yourself before. I am also trying to discover my sense of fashion around my altered body habitus.

Take a Bow (2015–2018)

This collection is about top hats, bows and a playful spirit.
Embracing change and having fun with it.

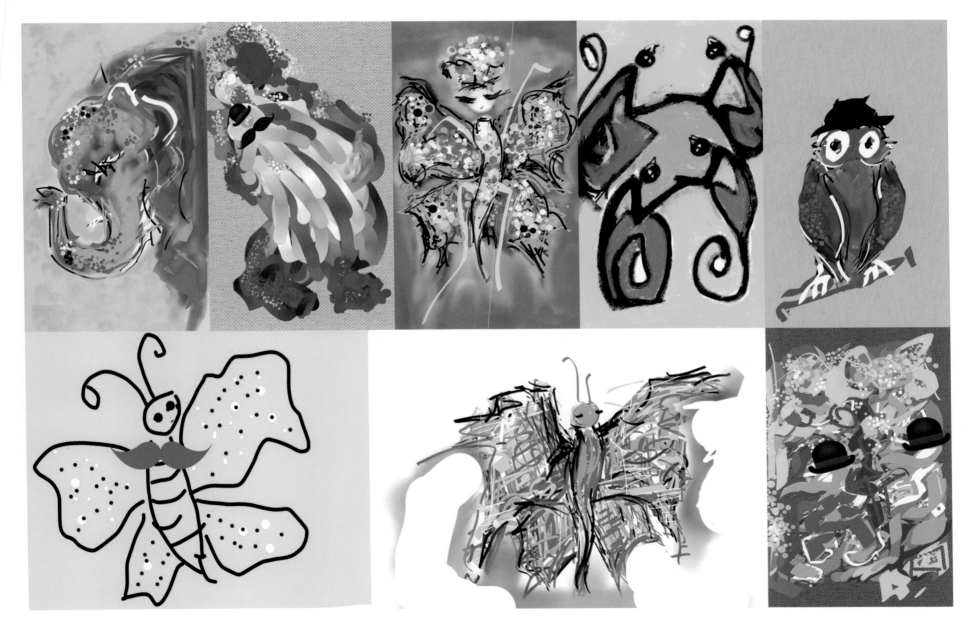

Up the Tempo (2015–2019)

This collection is about rhythm and movement and a vibrant spirit. It ranges from dancing human figures to doctor cats and bees wearing sunglasses, music notes, festive butterflies, to studious elephants and funky spiders.

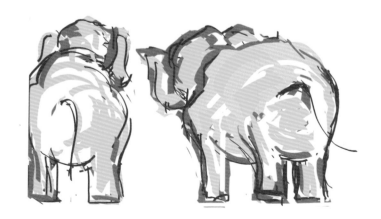

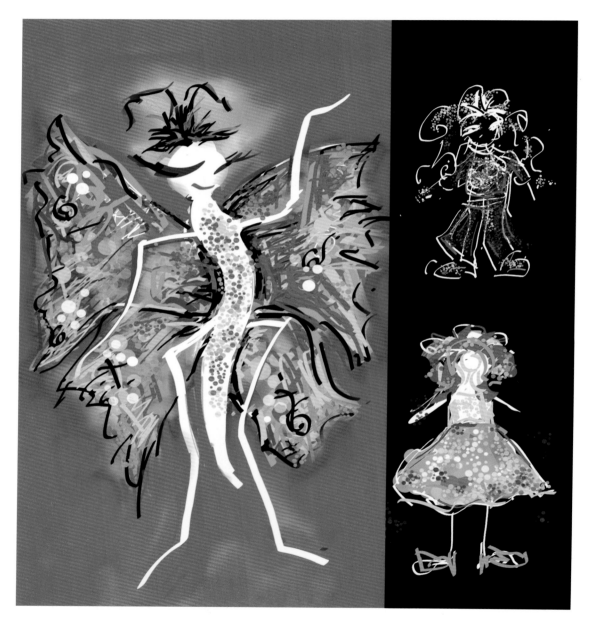

256

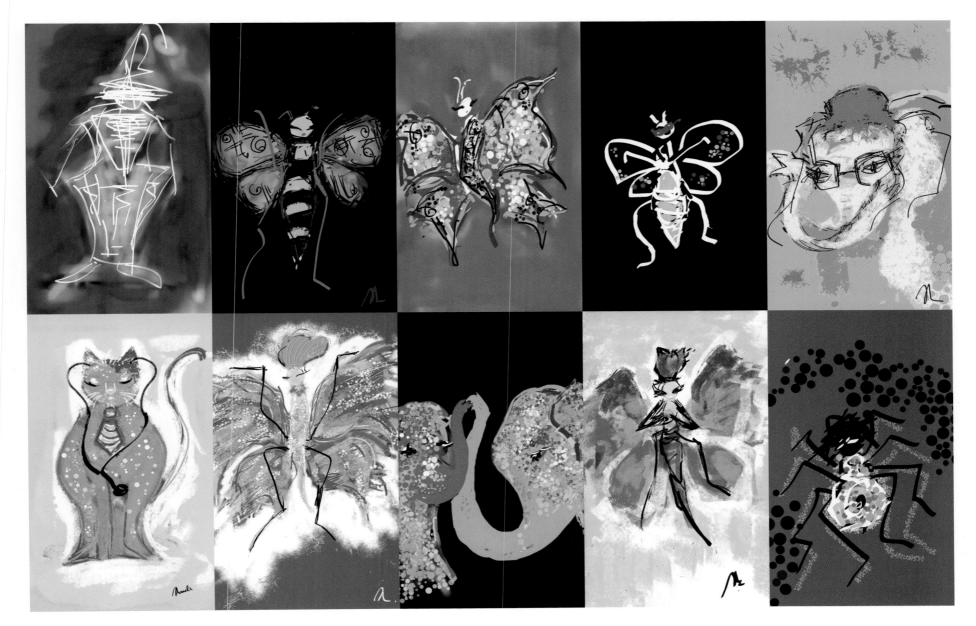

Sunny Side Up (2016–2020)

This collection is about lively colours and uplifting the spirit.
A ray of brightness and cheer …

Trumpet Calls (2017–2019)

This collection draws on the greeting spirit of elephants.

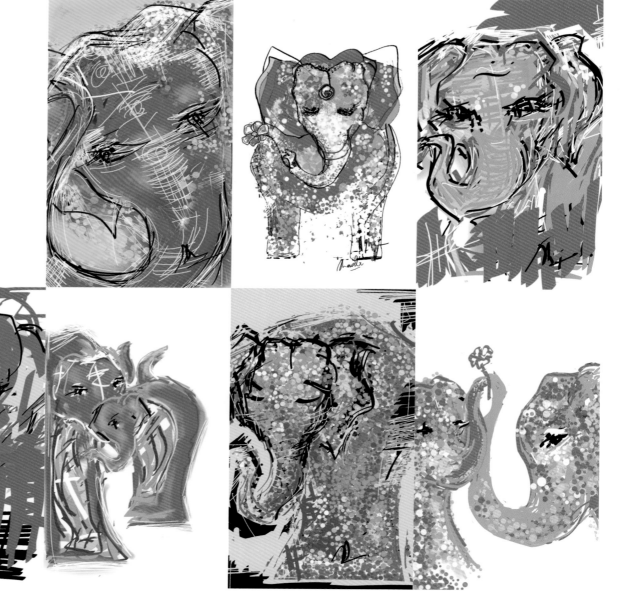

Symmetry (2017–2019)

This collection is about silhouettes, reels, swirls and wheels forming repetitive symmetrical patterns translating the intriguing spirit of moods and feelings. The spiral progression is symbolic of finding symmetry in whirls of chaos during my days of 'the calm, the storm and the in-between'. It is a route to achieving balance within. The spiral and the vortex point to dynamic inner movements, indicating the transformation and the integration of physical, emotional and spiritual elements. Together they constitute the journey and change of life as it unfolds and the inner growth that takes place.

Spirals (2017–2019)

Spirals are one of the oldest geometric shapes found throughout the ancient world, dating back to around the Neolithic period 12,000 years ago. It is fascinating that people belonging to different cultures in separate continents with no direct contact all carved similar spiral symbols. Carl Jung, the Swiss psychiatrist, said that the spiral is the perfect model of our representation of the universe. The spiral is the age-old intuitive symbol that represents how we identify with the cosmic force.

Still (2019)

This collection is about the spirit of life. It is the start and finish of life's journey depicted in lines, shapes and contours as it twists and turns, experiencing different shades of black, white and grey before coming to a halt, at the end, when all stands still. The images here illustrate our life cycle from start to finish, with all of its fluctuations, the happy and the sad, showing how our thoughts, feelings and actions interact with one another. The image on the right, which has more shades of grey, emphasises the many uncertainties we face as we walk through life.

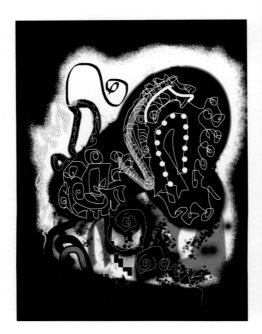

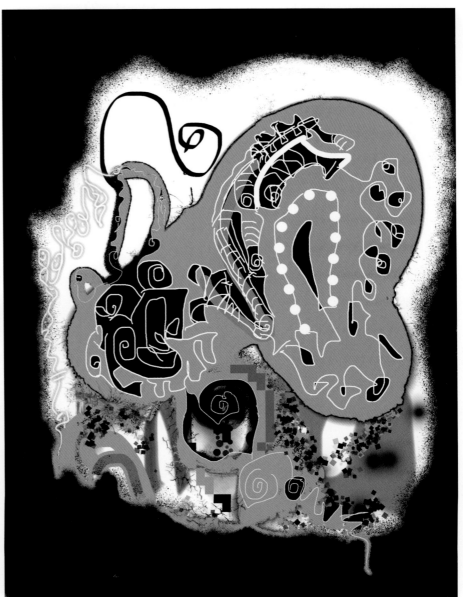

This is part of the *Still* series that shows life in colour. All the colours here portray different energies, capturing our life rhythms at different points in time. We keep changing these colours as we progress through life, reacting to the challenges and experiences we encounter. Depending on the impact these encounters have on our lives, the shades and tones of the colours will change accordingly. The impact may be good or bad; they may make us feel alive and vibrant or dampen our spirit. The red, orange and yellow in these images show vibrancy and cheer. The purple and blue tones are more neutral. Green conveys balance, connecting us to our inner and outer worlds. The black and white define dark and light feelings, and grey is the in-between moods.

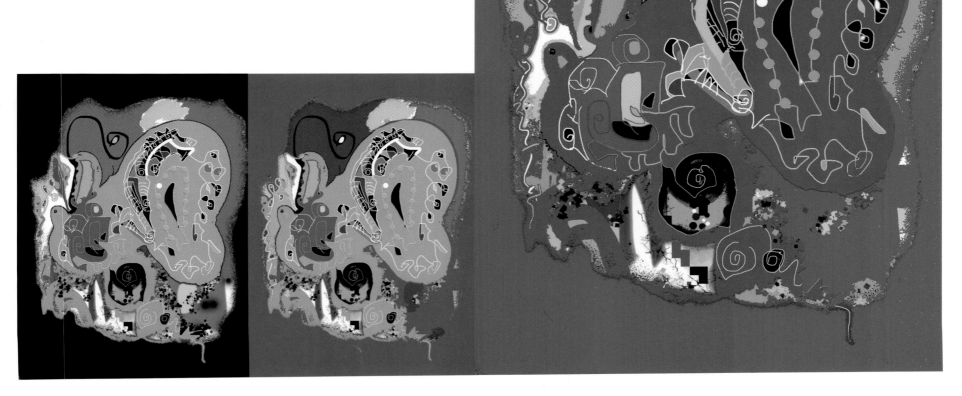

What Next?
Moving Forward as Me

'My mission in life is not merely to survive,
but to thrive; and to do so with some
passion, some compassion, some
humour, and some style.'

Maya Angelou

Summary: what I aim to achieve with my art

As the founder of Changing Lanes, I am working across the intersections of art, health, medical education and patient support.

Creating digital art has had a transformative impact in helping me to manage living with my rare long-term illness. Having a tool such as art, alongside medication and other therapies, allowed me to cope, adapt and change as I adjusted to life with a chronic condition.

Through my art, I hope to generate public awareness on:

- The **life-changing course** that invisible, inflammatory conditions tend to have on patients and the ripple effects they cause on their lives

- Bridging the gap between the **biomedical and the human focus**

- The **impact long-term illness** can have on a person's image, self-identity and self-esteem

- The bigger picture, focusing on a better understanding of **invisible illnesses and stigma**

- The **role of art in long-term illness** and its use in the multidisciplinary approaches to the self-management of illness

- **The potential therapeutic benefits** of linking creative empowerment as a nondrug intervention to assist in promoting health and healing

- Harnessing the **creative side constructively** to refine adjustment strategies, finding new ways to adapt to long-term conditions **to cope** with day-to-day challenges, as well as having fun

- **Promoting the role of the digital medium: creativity made easy** for people with physical restrictions or limitations in hand function to access tools for art and creativity

The focus of my art

- Start more conversations on how 'creative force' empowered me

- Highlight the impact of illness on image, self-identity and stigma

- Biomedical focus **< interconnect >** human focus

- Connect and collaborate with others in the field of arts and health

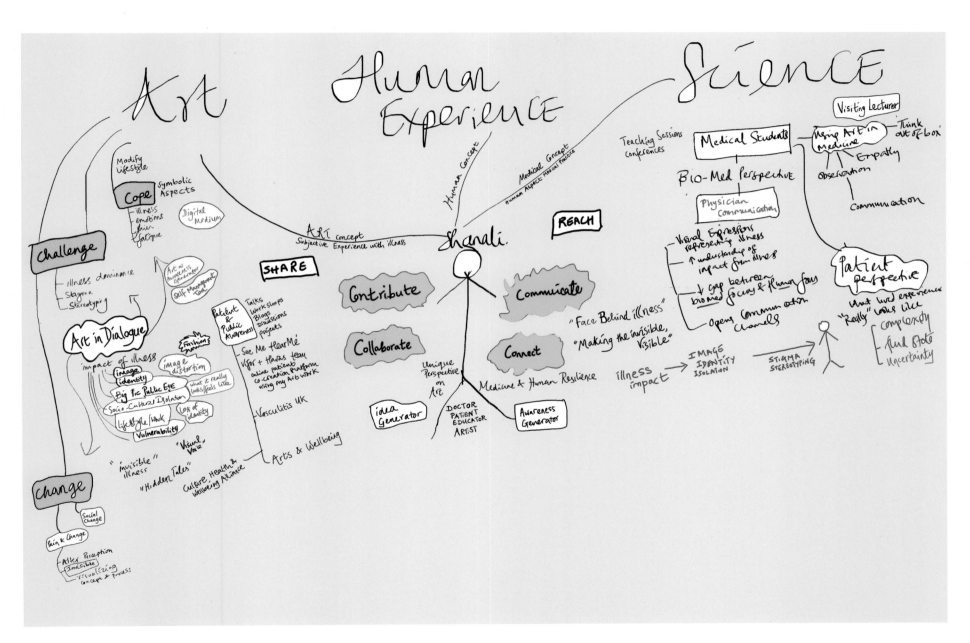

What is it that my art does?

Illness can affect every aspect of a person's life. Art enabled me to take chances and champion ideas and enriched me with new knowledge and experiences.

I am interested in looking at the extent of how the visual arts can help us further explore our understanding of the human focus of medical science and the human condition and expand our awareness of empathy. I hope my visual narrative presented in this book connects with you and shows all the interrelationships that come into play in a person's illness journey. I also hope it provides you with newer insights into the different influences governing the illness trajectory.

- How do we, as a collective, step out of the comfort zone and narrow the gap between medical science and human experience?

- What part can you play as a caring fellow co-human?

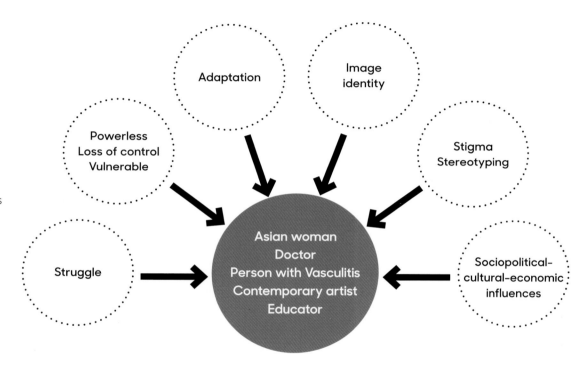

'Where there is love for humanity, there is also love for art.'

Hippocrates, the father of Western medicine

Food for thought: accepting pain or change visually

- When you think of pain or change, what colour comes to mind? What shape comes to mind?

- Would visualising the process and concept of pain or change make you see it differently?

- Would you see it in a different light, or a different angle or perspective?

- In essence, does visually capturing the invisible subjective world of feeling, by constructing a structure for it, make a meaningful difference?

- For me, being able to construct the concept and process visually helped to better accept the changes brought on by the illness – it also showed me ways to communicate what I was going through to myself and others.

- I hope my visual capture of the subjective embodiment of pain and change connects with you.

- Would adding this sensory dimension help alter perceptions and be impactful in healthcare communication?

- Will it help to see more of the face, the person behind the illness with multiple dimensions?

- Will it open ways to improve current clinical practice, medical education and its future direction?

- Would this in turn help to narrow the gap between the biomedical perspective on disease and the patient-led perspective of illness?

What do you think?

Take-home messages

- Creativity is a reservoir of healing – it offers a means to take control of and construct a positive identity.

- So why not put this into wider use in the context of the self-management of chronic illnesses and disability?

- Why not use art to challenge the dominance caused by illness or disability?

- As a personal narrative as well as a record, visual storytelling with art helped me immensely to face overwhelming periods during my patient journey.

Why not take a closer look at your creative space?

Finding Me Beyond Illness

Right: *Connection*, 2018
Opposite: *Stolen Moments*, 2018

'I see the person beyond the illness
Where the illness ends, I begin …

I see me now
Do you see me?'

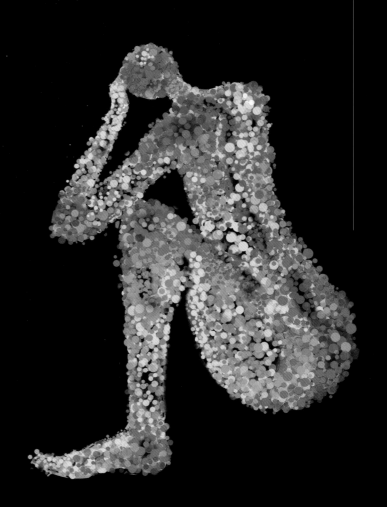

© 2022 Shanali Perera

First Edition

Shanali Perera asserts the moral right to be identified
as the author of this work in accordance with the
Copyright, Designs and Patents Act 1988.

ISBN 978-1-8383221-0-6

Book design by Adam Hay Studio
Edited by Ian Fitzgerald

All rights reserved. No part of this publication may be
reproduced, distributed, or transmitted in any form or by any
means, including photocopying, recording, or other electronic
or mechanical methods, without the prior written permission of
the publisher, except in the case of brief quotations embodied in
critical reviews and certain other noncommercial uses permitted
by copyright law. For permission requests, write to the author at
shanaliperera@gmail.com.

Printed in Sri Lanka by
Softwave Printing and Packaging (Pvt) Ltd
No. 107D, Havelock Road, Colombo 5, Sri Lanka

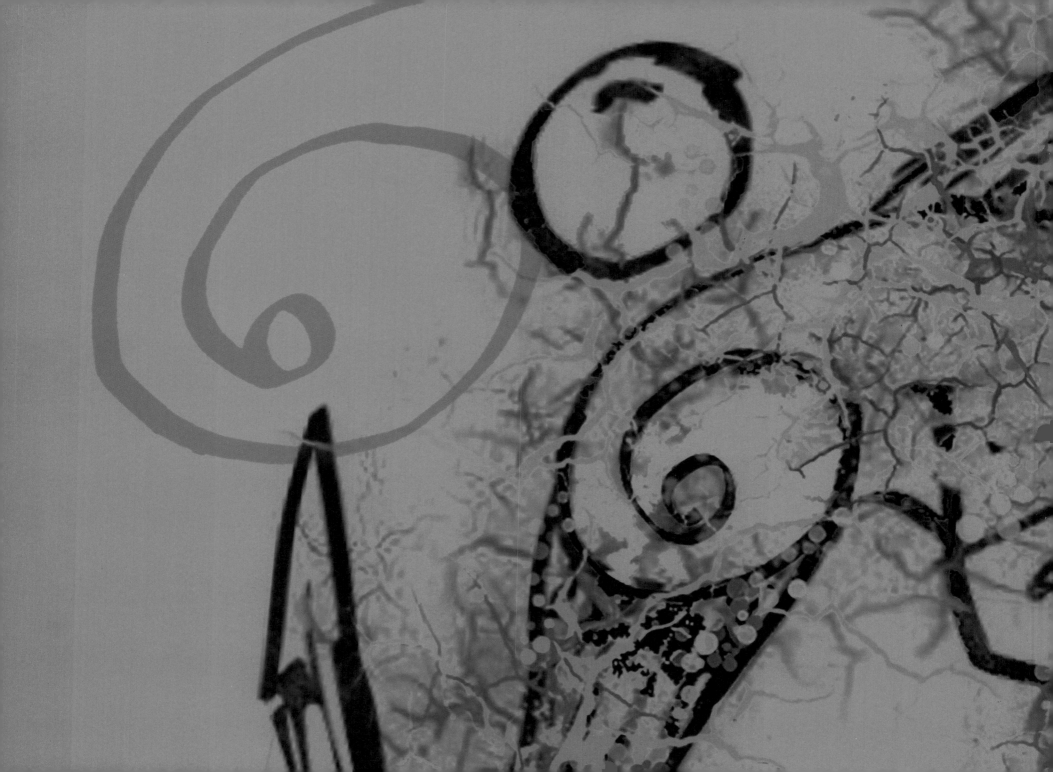